Expansion and Contraction Within Being
(Dahm)

Molana Salaheddin Ali Nader Shah Angha
"Pir Oveyssi"

M.T.O. Shahmaghsoudi® Publications

M.T.O. SHAHMAGHSOUDI® PUBLICATIONS

Angha, Molana Salaheddin Ali Nader Shah "Pir Oveyssi"

Expansion & Contraction Within Being
(Dahm)

Library of Congress Card Number: 00-192726
ISBN: 0-910735-61-1
Printed in the U.S.A.

Published by M.T.O. Shahmaghsoudi
Printing and Publication Center
10590 Magnolia Ave., Suite G
Riverside, CA 92505 - U.S.A.
e-mail: angha_rs@pacbell.net

M.T.O. Shahmaghsoudi Headquarters
5225 Wisconsin Ave., N.W., Suite 502
Washington, D.C. 20015 - U.S.A.
e-mail: mtos@cais.com
website: http://mto.shahmaghsoudi.org

First Edition Published:
May 10, 2001

Muon Radiation Therapy: Patent Pending
Neuron Network Modeling: Patent Pending
Gravitational Force Modifying Apparatus: Patent Pending

Other books by the same author:

The Approaching Promise

The Fragrance of Sufism

Masnavi Ravayeh

Peace

The Secret Word

Sufi Lecture Series:

(Sufism, Sufism and Wisdom,

Sufism and Islam, Sufism and Peace,

Sufism and Knowledge)

Sufism: The Reality of Religion

Whispering Moments: Inspirations

Revelation

TABLE OF CONTENTS

<u>Section:</u>   **<u>Page:</u>**

CHAPTER 1

FUSION IN MITOCHONDRION RESPIRATION

1- INTRODUCTION

We have come a long way toward understanding the chemical reactions that lead to Adenosine TriPhospate (ATP) production (in mitochondria, choloroplasts, and bacteria).[1-3] Through these advances, the chemical chain reaction in the production of ATP seems to be well understood.[1-3] In spite of these advances the actual ATP production mechanism, i.e., the very *mechanism* of respiration is most probably far from being thoroughly understood.[1] We seem to comprehend the chemical processes leading to ATP synthesis. Yet we have very little appreciation of how the initial energy produced by the oxidation of the carbohydrates is transferred from one stage to the other and how much energy protons require in order for the synthesizing of ATP to take place.

Perhaps the most universally accepted theory for ATP production is the chemiosmotic theory that Peter Mitchell suggested in 1961.[4] Mitchell's theory claims that the proton (H^+) density difference between the inside and the outside of the mitochondrion inner membrane produces the electrical potential energy that is needed to accelerate the protons, leading to ATP production.

However, it is believed that Mitchell's theory ignores an important aspect in mitochondrion's respiration and does not properly address the source of energy which drives the protons to the mitochondrion's intermembrane space and which is also primarily responsible for ATP synthesis.

Mitchell clearly and brilliantly explains the chemical processes through which protons are deposited in the intermembrane space.[4] However, the main source of energy leading to this deposition and subsequent protonation of the F_0-F_1 enzyme[1-8] is overlooked. This leads me to agree that it is indeed the protonation of the "F_0-F_1 enzyme" which is responsible for ATP production. Nevertheless, I will attempt to show that the mere energy gained through the potential difference across the inner membrane is not adequate for the protonation of F_0-F_1 enzyme (or ATP synthesis).

2 - THE MITOCHONDRION

The metabolic energy of the eukaryotic cells (cells in which the genetic material is contained) is mostly localized within mitochondria. In essence, except for ten reactions of the glycolytic pathway, all of the ATP of the eukaryotes is generated within the mitochondrion.[2,3]

Mitochondria are typically 0.7-1 μm in length.[1,2] Their shape is not fixed; it varies continuously within the cell. Each mitochondrion has two membranes. The outer membrane is permeable to molecules with a molecular mass of 5000 Dalton or less.[2] This degree of permeability does not make the outer membrane a significant barrier to most molecules. Consequently the inter-membrane space (space between the inner and the outer membrane) is occupied by plasma. Nonetheless, the inner membrane is highly selective and non-permeable to most molecules. The only substances that cross the inner membrane are those that participate in active transport; i.e., pyruvates, citrates, Ca^{2+}, phosphates, Mg^{2+}, inorganic phosphorus, ADP, ATP, molecular oxygen, etc.[2] Also contained in the intermembrane space are the H^+ nuclei or protons. These protons are deposited as a result of carbohydrate breakdown that will be discussed in the next section. The remaining space in the mitochondrion is called the matrix; it is gel-like, and contains DNA molecules and ribosomes.[2] The mitochondrion has the capacity to produce some of the proteins it requires.

The mitochondrion density varies from cell to cell and also depends on the organ to which the cell belongs. For instance, there are only a few mitochondria per cell in fungi and algae, whereas each human liver cell has 500 to 1000 mitochondria. A typical cell such as an hepatocyte contains about 800 mitochondria.[3]

The inner membrane folds in on itself and provides a much larger surface area. This folding of the inner membrane is called the cristae. Knob-like spheres are elevated from the cristae. These spheres are called F_1 (fraction 1). They have a diameter of approximately 9.0 nm.[5] What remains after the removal of F_1 is called F_0. In essence, F_0 is the base of the knob, which is imbedded in the inner membrane itself.[5] These proteins are believed to be the enzymes that facilitate ATP production in mitochondrion respiration, and are called ATP synthetase or ATP-ase. Also F_0-F_1 is the actual pathway of the protons whose transfer of kinetic energy results in ATP synthesis.

3 - ELECTRON TRANSPORT AND MITCHELL'S THEORY

References one to six have discussed the electronic transport across the inner membrane and Mitchell's theory in detail.

The energy liberated through the complete breakdown or oxidation of glucose ($C_6H_{12}O_6 + 6O_2 \rightarrow 6CO_2 + 6H_2O$) is 686 kcal/mol[2]; which is equal to 29.76 eV/molecule. This is the kinetic energy of the glucose oxidation products (carbon dioxide and water molecules). Assuming low collision speeds are needed for oxygen and glucose molecules (i.e., zero initial speeds), and applying the conservation law of momentum and total energy, we can show that 29.0% of this energy (29.76 eV) goes to the $6CO_2$ molecules. The breakdown of glucose partially takes place through the TriCarboxilic Acid (TCA) cycle.[2,3,6] The oxygen breaks down the carbohydrates to carbon dioxide and Hydrogen. Then the hydrogen ion H^+ (the proton) is delivered to the ionized molecule Nicotinamide Adenine Dinucleotide (NAD^+).[2,3,6] If we assume that each H^+ carries 1/12 part (12 H atoms are released) of the rest of the energy released $[(1-0.29)X29.76]$ eV = 21.12 eV), then the kinetic energy of each H^+ is 1.76 eV.

Thus, in the mitochondrion matrix, the NAD^+ **accepts one hydrogen ion from this breakdown** and two electrons and converts itself to NADH.[2-7] The NADH then travels toward the inner membrane of the mitochondrion and the respiration process starts. In this process the enzymes located in the inner mitochondrial membrane ultimately deliver the two electrons gained by NAD^+ to oxygen, which then takes two protons from the environment and the result, is the formation of water molecules.

The process of respiration is as follows: The NADH molecule loses two electrons and one proton to Flavin MonoNucleotide (FMN), an intermediary enzyme.[2-7] Therefore, the NADH goes back to NAD^+ and FMN **takes another proton from the inner membrane** and converts this to $FMNH_2$. These two protons are then released into the mitochondrial intermembrane space; the two electrons travel to two Iron Sulfur (FeS) centers.[2-7] The FeS centers are tightly bound to their proteins and the combination forms another mitochondrial inner membrane enzyme. Consequently, $FMNH_2$ is converted back to the form FMN, which can again be reduced to $FMNH_2$. Unlike FMN, FeS centers participate only in single electron transfer reactions.[3,4,6] Neither center carries any proton. These types of present FeS centers depend on the number of iron and sulfur atoms. As many as one, two, four, or more atoms of iron and sulfur are found in FeS centers. The electrons delivered to the FeS centers are eventually transferred back to the matrix of the mitochondrion.

In the next stage of respiration, FeS centers deliver the two electrons to two ubiquinone molecules or coenzyme Q.[2-7] Each coenzyme Q takes one electron from a FeS center and then one proton from the mitochondrial matrix to form the semiquinone molecule ($QH^.$).[6] Each semiquinone molecule accepts one electron from a cytocrome b (a protein with an iron which can accept or donate an electron: embedded in the inner membrane of the mitochondrion) and a proton from the matrix of the mitochondrion to form two hydroquinone QH_2 molecules. Each of the two QH_2 molecules, which are mobile in the inner membrane, donates one of its electrons to a cytochrome c_1 and **deposits a proton in the intermembrane space.** The other two electrons are transferred to a cytochorome b and **the remaining**

two protons are delivered to the intermembrane space. The two electrons (delivered to cytochrome c_1) are then delivered to cytochromes c, a, and a_3.[1-3,6,7] In cytochrome a_3, the two electrons, two protons from the inside of the innermembrane, and an oxygen form a water molecule.[1-3,6,7] **Consequently in each respiratory cycle six protons are transferred from the inside of the inner membrane to its outside; i.e., the intermembrane plasma.**[1-7]

According to Mitchell, the deposition of the protons in the intermembrane space produces an Electric Potential Difference (EPD) between the inside and the outside of the inner membrane.[8] Giving the protons a kinetic energy, this EPD delivers them back to the inside of the matrix.[8] The protons, however, enter the matrix through F_0-F_1 knobs. Observations indicate that the F_0 part of the knobs serves only as a channel through which protons cross the membrane to F_1 which is the actual site of the ATP synthesis.[1,6] The mechanism of the ATP synthesis in F_1 is not yet understood, although there have been many proposals by Mitchell and others.[1,6] It is believed that the synthesis of ATP from ADP and inorganic Phosphorous (P_i) can take place spontaneously if both molecules were bound to a protein.[6] The release of ATP however, needs additional energy. It is believed that the kinetic energy of the protons gained through the EPD of the innermembrane is responsible for a conformational change leading to the release of the bound ATP.[1,6]

4-THE WEAKNESSES OF MITCHELL'S THEORY

Many references in scientific literature indicate that the chemiosmotic theory is speculative, especially when it comes to the "Q cycle" of the electron transport.[6] This presentation will attempt to indicate at least two other deficiencies in Mitchell's theory.

As mentioned in section 3, the kinetic energy that the proton (produced by the breakdown of carbohydrates and subsequently delivered to NAD^+) carries is about 1.76 eV. Generally, protons, which are released into the matrix of the mitochondrion quickly, dissolve in water and form molecules of Hydronium (Hy) H_3O^+. Taking the temperature of the matrix as T = 310 K, then according to the kinetic theory of gasses, the average kinetic energy of each Hydronium ion is KE = (3/2)kT or 0.040 eV. Here, k = 1.38×10^{-23} J.molecule^{-1}.K^{-1}; is the Boltzman constant. Thus, in the respiratory cycle every time a proton is taken from the matrix, that proton has a kinetic energy of 0.040 eV. As discussed in section 3, this happens five times in the respiratory cycle.[6] On the other hand, when ATP generation starts, the EPD between the matrix and the intermembrane space is about 0.22 V.[1] Let us take the average EPD even considerably lower i.e., as 0.15 V. In this case each proton which has to be deposited in the intermembrane space should have at least 0.15 eV of kinetic energy. Also when the hydrogen atoms are ionized[6] at the exterior surface of the inner membrane, this ionization needs energy. The question is where does the energy of ionization as well as the energy needed for the deposition of the protons into the intermembrane space, come from? The protons that are taken from the inside of the mitochondrion do not have enough kinetic energy (average KE = 0.040 eV). Nor do they gain energy in their path to the intermembrane space because their binding energy to flavin mononucleotide FMN and ubiquinone Q is released into the matrix.[6] Furthermore, the mechanism of the hydrogen atom transfer from the matrix to the outer surface of the inner membrane is a mystery.[6] Thus, contrary to general belief, it is more convincing to conclude that the glucose breakdown energy is released into the matrix. It is largely spent on providing thermal energy for the system rather than being spent for ATP generation.

As I mentioned earlier, it is hypothesized[6] that the kinetic energy of the protons gained through the inner membrane EPD is spent on ATP synthesis.[1-8] The EPD between the two faces of the inner membrane is about 0.22 V.[1] The kinetic energy gained by a proton through this EPD is therefore 0.22 eV. Subsequently it takes two protons to synthesize one ATP, the total available energy is then 0.44 eV. In their collision with the inorganic phosphorous P_i, or the ADP molecule, the two protons transfer energy to them. More energy is transferred if we presuppose the protons collide with the inorganic phosphorous rather than the ADP. Taking the initial speed of the P_i (v_{iP_i}) as equal to zero and applying the laws of conservation of momentum and kinetic energy, we can find the fraction of the energy that is transferred to the P_i. For elastic and inelastic collisions, the energy transferred To the P_i is $4(M_{p_i}/m_{H^+})(m_{H^+}/M_{P_i}+m_{H^+})^2$ KE_{H^+} and $(M_{P_i}/m_{H^+})(m_{H^+}/M_{P_i}+m_{H^+})^2 KE_{H^+}$ respectively. Inasmuch as $M_{P_i} \approx 31\ m_{H^+}$ and $KE_{H^+} = 0.44$ eV, these energies amount to 0.048 eV and 0.012 eV respectively. Therefore more energy is transferred for the elastic collision of the protons with the P_i. Consequently the two protons can contribute at most

0.048 eV to ATP synthesis; while ATP synthesis needs approximately 0.35 eV (approx. equivalent to 8 kcal/mol[2,3]). **In an elastic collision between two protons and the P_i, each proton must have at least 1.45 eV of initial kinetic energy in order to transfer 0.35 eV to the P_i.**

Based on these observations, Mitchell's theory disregards the fact that there is insuffcient energy to transport the protons to the intermembrane space as well as to synthesize ATP. These circumstances bring about the search for another source of kinetic energy for the protons, a source that provides enough kinetic energy for the protons to:

A)   Channel through the enzymes,

B)   Break themselves away from the electrons,

C)   Push their way into the higher EPD of the intermembrane space, and

D)   On their way back into the matrix, through F_0-F_1 enzyme have enough kinetic energy to synthesize and release ATP.

I contend that the only way to solve these questions and perhaps other questions regarding the mechanism of ATP generation is to look for a new source of energy. A source, which increases the kinetic energy of the inside and outside matrix protons to much higher values (almost 10 times more).

5 - THE MAIN SOURCE OF ENERGY IN A MITOCHONDRION

As far as bioscience has been able to ascertain, protons are indeed taken from the inside and deposited in the outside of the inner membrane. Additionally, experimental evidence points out the fact that the passage of the protons through the F_0-F_1 enzyme results in ATP release.[1,6] Therefore, there must be enough energy for these processes to take place; the source of which has not been identified.

At this point, *I assert that this source of energy is of nuclear origin; mainly catalyzed fusion[9] energy.* Basically, I believe the fusion of a proton (H^+) and a Deuterium (D) nuclei, two D nuclei, or a D and a Tritium (T) nuclei within the mitochondrion or in the intermembrane space is the main source of kinetic energy for the proton transfer and an eventual release of ATP.

The energy released in a e.g. D-D fusion is at least 3.26 MeV which manifests itself in the form of the kinetic energy of the particles produced e.g., neutrons.[9] In the matrix of mitochondrion and in its intermembrane space, the fast mo products of the fusion collide with the H atoms and H^+ ions; and the enormous amount of kinetic energy from the products of the fusion is transferred basically to the hydrogen atoms and H^+ ions. This occurs because the proteins and enzyme molecules are much more massive than the hydrogen atoms or the H^+ ions (the protons) and therefore do not move nearly as fast. Then the H^+ ions will have enough kinetic energy to channel through the enzymes to the intermembrane space. Their kinetic energy (gained through collisions with the fusion products, i.e., neutrons) will push them into the intermembrane space against the EPD; and the collision of these H^+ ions with those in the intermembrane space will bring about increased kinetic energy exchange. This observation demonstrates that during ATP synthesis the kinetic energy of the protons is much higher than approximately 0.22 eV. I concur that this is indeed the EPD

ween the matrix and the intermembrane space responsible for

ton flow through F_0-F_1 knobs back into the matrix. I refer

gained through this EPD as the drift velocity.

electric conduction in wires, here the protons have

d consequently thermal velocity as well. The

hypothesis could be numerous. However,

before discussing this hypothesis any further, I would like to present a short review of catalyzed fusion as well as cosmic rays.

6 - COLD FUSION OR MUON CATALYZED FUSION

The word fusion usually suggests to us the need for temperatures as high as those do at the core of the sun, powerful magnets, and electric charge plasma concentrated by powerful lasers.[9,10] This ordinary type of fusion requires high temperatures. At high enough temperatures the kinetic energy of the H^+ ions is proportionally high.   Thus, the electrostatic repulsion among the H^+ ions is not powerful enough to keep the protons apart and fusion takes place. The muon-catalyzed fusion, however, eliminates the need for high temperatures.[9,10]

One type of muon, namely an elementary particle, has an electric charge equal to that of the electron but is about 207 times more massive than the electron. These short-lived elementary particles are produced when primary cosmic ray, primarily containing very fast protons, collides with the upper atmosphere. The average muon's lifetime in its own rest frame is 2.2×10^{-6} seconds.[11] Ordinarily this lifetime is not long enough for the muons to reach the earth's surface. However, since these muons' speed is very close to that of light c ($= 3x10^8$ m/s), the relativistic time dilation takes effect. Thus, according to the stationary observer on earth, the muons live much longer than $2.2X10^{-6}$ seconds do and they do indeed reach us.

F. C. Frank and Andrei D. Sakharov first suggested the muon-catalyzed fusion in the late 1940's. Commonly in the Deuterium (D) atom the electron is relatively far away from the nucleus. The D atom is an isotope of the H atom. In the nucleus of the D atom there is a proton and a neutron. The laws of quantum mechanics indicate that the shortest possible radius of the electron in the D atom, i.e., the Bohr radius, is about $0.5X10^{-8}$ cm. The faster ($v \approx c$) and 207 times more massive muon collides with the electron orbiting the D nucleus and knocks it off. It replaces the electron and forms Muonic Deuterium (MD). Quantum mechanics indicate that the radius of an orbit is inversely proportional to the mass of the orbiting particle. Once the electrons are replaced by negative muons, this shortest orbital radius is reduced by a factor of 207; consequently, MD is 207 times smaller than the D atom. This can be the key to the "cold fusion" of the muonic atoms i.e., MD. The short orbital radius of the muon makes the muonic atom appear as a neutral particle to distant particles. At ordinary temperatures such a muonic atom can collide with another muonic atom to form a mumolecule.[9] The nuclei of mumolecules are much closer to each other than they are in ordinary deuterium molecules. Thus, the fusion of these nuclei can and does take place at ordinary temperatures.[9] This is due to the fact that the nuclei are close to each other and there is no need for high kinetic energies or high temperatures.

After fusion has taken place, the muon is ejected in most cases. Thus, it is free to catalyze another fusion. The energy produced by the fusion is released in the form of kinetic energy of the neutrons; and these neutrons are in turn ejected as a product of the fusion. The products of the fusion of two MD atoms could be a Helium three, ^{3}He nucleus and a neutron. If the atoms in the mumolecule are an MD atom and a Tritium (T) atom, then the product of the fusion is an alpha particle and a neutron. The T atom is an isotope of H with two neutrons and the alpha particle is the nucleus of the Helium four ^{4}He atom. The total time it takes for the muon to be captured and catalyze the fusion can be made less than a thousandth of the muon's lifetime.[9]

The 3.26 MeV (1 eV is 1.6×10^{-19} Joules) is the energy gained through one route of fusion. In fact, the fusion of D-D can produce ^{3}He or T. If T is produced, the gained energy is 4.03 MeV. Subsequently, the T can fuse with another D to produce ^{4}He and a neutron and 17.6 MeV. Accordingly, the average energy gained in the H isotopes fusion is 8.3 MeV.

Luis W. Alvarez et al. at Berkeley presented the first experimental evidence of muon-catalyzed fusion in the late 1950's.[9] Since that time the physicists have continued working on theoretical and experimental muon-catalyzed fusion. However, their efforts to make muon-catalyzed fusion economically feasible have not been successful. *"Cold nuclear fusion, whether caused by muons or particles other than muons, is presently the focus of considerable present interest and research. If it does not turn out to be a serious contender for an economically viable method of generating energy, it at least demonstrates that fusion, in general, can be initiated by means simpler than high-temperature plasmas or giant lasers".*[10] *"The zoo of the elementary particles is a large one, and it is conceivable that some particles other than muon might also be able to catalyze fusion".*[9]

7 - Cosmic Rays

Since cosmic rays play an important role in muon catalyzed fusion I would like to briefly cover them before returning to the discussion of cold fusion in a mitochondrion.

Cosmic rays were discovered as a result of an increase in the conductivity and thus the ionization of a gas as a function of altitude. Gockel, Hess, and Kolhoster made this discovery before 1914.[12] An ionization chamber was sent up into the atmosphere and the gas conductivity was measured. Keeping the gas temperature constant, the number of ionized molecules first started to decrease up to 2000 feet elevation; and subsequently increased up to the highest altitude their balloon could reach. These observers proposed the existence of an ionizing radiation that reaches the earth surface from outer space. The fact that the ionization was hardly affected by nightfall led to the conclusion that this radiation must not come from the sun. Eventually this radiation was called cosmic radiation. Initially, it was thought that cosmic rays consisted mainly of high-energy photons. But later, with the development of new sophisticated detecting devices, it became clear that a large portion of the radiation consisted of charged particles. These charged particles were mainly positrons and μ mesons or muons. Cosmic radiation at sea level can be divided into two parts. The first part is the soft component which is absorbed before penetrating a lead plate of 10 cm thickness. The second part is the hard component, which does penetrate beyond 10 cm of lead.

Cosmic radiation, which originally enters the earth's atmosphere from outer space, is called primary radiation. The radiation produced by the collision of this primary radiation with atmospheric particles is called secondary radiation. It is this secondary radiation, which is received at sea level, that penetrates the human body.[12,13]

Experiments indicate that the constituents of primary radiation are mainly protons and the stable nuclei of the elements. Tracks of nuclei of the elements from helium to iron, i.e., $Z = 2$ to 26 has been observed in the detectors. No nucleus heavier than iron has been detected in cosmic ray radiation. In their path through the atmosphere, the heavy nuclei collide with air molecules and very soon break into lighter nuclei. Thus, within the earth's atmosphere the lighter charged particles are much more abundant than the heavier charged ones. The relative abundance of protons, α-particles, and the heavier nuclei in the primary cosmic ray is j_p: j_α: $j_{heavier}$ = 1: 1/7: 1/60. Here, j_p, j_α, and $j_{heavier}$ refer to the flux of protons, α-particles or the nuclei of the ^{4}He atom, and the heavier nuclei, respectively.[13] The abundance of electrons and photons in primary radiation has been established to be less than 0.25%.

As mentioned earlier, the daily or the ordinary solar effect on the intensity of cosmic radiation is very insignificant. Additionally, no significant change in the radiation intensity is observed through 27 lunar days. On the other hand, the effect of solar flares on this intensity is considerable. In one experiment the solar flares resulted in a threefold increase for primary radiation of energy 10-100 GeV (1GeV = 1 X10^9 eV). For the primary radiation of energy 1-10 GeV the increase was 50 times. Thus, at least under certain conditions, there is a considerable contribution from the sun in the cosmic rays reaching the earth's surface. It has been established that the high-energy portion of the primary radiation originates from outside the solar system.[13]

When this primary radiation enters the earth's atmosphere, its particles go through multiple collisions with the atmospheric particles. As a result of these interactions, the protons in the primary radiation produce particles called π mesons with a lifetime of about 2.5×10^{-8}s, i.e., about one hundredth of a muon's lifetime. The π meson decays to a muon and another particle called a neutrino. The speed of these muons is very close to that of light; furthermore, they travel through the atmosphere with almost no colliding. Special relativity laws can show that it takes almost no time for the muons to arrive at the earth's surface. Actually, at near sea level the whole portion of the penetrating or hard component of secondary radiation is composed of muons.[12] At higher altitudes, the soft component of secondary radiation consists of electrons, low energy mesons, and protons. Thus, at sea level the most important part of charged cosmic radiation consists entirely of muons. Considering the lifetime of the muons and the average distance they have to travel to reach the surface of the earth, their energy must be greater than 2 GeV.[12] The total intensity of the hard component of the cosmic rays at sea level is 200 $m^{-2}s^{-1}$.[11] The other important component of cosmic radiation at sea level is the electronic component with an intensity of about one third the total radiation at sea level.[12]

8 - COLD FUSION IN A MITOCHONDRION

As noted earlier, the main part of the hard component cosmic ray is composed of muons that consist of at least 2 GeV of energy. These muons obviously penetrate our bodies down to the cellular and even to the atomic level. It was also mentioned in section four that there is a reservoir of hydrogen atoms and H^+ ions in mitochondria. The natural abundance rate of D to H is $1/6000$.[10] This means that in one mole of hydrogen there are as many as $6.02 \times 10^{23}/6000 \approx 1 \times 10^{20}$ of Deuterium. The existence of muons in the environment and the presence of the D atoms in the matrix of the mitochondrion inevitably mean that muon-catalyzed fusion could indeed take place in mitochondria. It is my belief that this is the main source of kinetic energy for hydrogen atoms and protons in the mitochondria; and suggest the following mechanism for this process.

The muons catalyze as many fusions as possible throughout their path in the mitochondria. In the next section we will observe that the energy produced merely by this first stage of fusion is insufficient. However, one should note that the energy produced through each fusion is 8.3 MeV. This energy is released in the form of the kinetic energy of the ejected neutrons and the He nuclei produced through the fusion. Obviously, these fast particles could, and I believe do, indeed catalyze many more fusions. This assumption, namely, that the products of the initial fusion catalyze further fusion's is nothing new.[14] In fact, it is known that in an environment of D atoms, fast neutrons can transfer part of their energy to the D atoms in a collision and harvest fusion. The problem in industry has been that the energy gained is insufficient to provide the D fuel as well as a usable economical surplus.[14] In essence, the rate of fusion and not its occurrence has been the problem.

Using Coulomb's law of electrostatic repulsion between the nuclei of two D atoms, one can calculate the energy needed to bring the nuclei together to a distance of r_0. If we take r_0 to be roughly the same as the nuclear radius, i.e., $r_0 = 5 \times 10^{-13}$ cm, then the energy of repulsion for two D nuclei is approximately 0.29 MeV. Furthermore, as we have mentioned, the average energy produced by a D-D fusion is 8.3 MeV. The fusion energy manifests itself as the kinetic energy of the neutrons and the He atom. Using the conservation laws of momentum and energy, one can show that in an elastic collision with a D nucleus at rest, these particles transfer as much as 89% of this energy (0.89X8.3 = 7.39 MeV) to the D nucleus. Using the conservation law of linear momentum, one can show that for inelastic collision of a neutron or an α particle with a D nucleus the kinetic energy of the system after collision is not less than 0.33% of the available energy (0.33X8.3 = 2.7 MeV). These energies are from 9 to 25 times greater than needed to fuse the D nuclei; hence we can expect a secondary fusion. These secondary products, I conclude, yield more fusions; and in fact a chain of fusion reactions takes place in our bodies.

9 - THE POSSIBILITY OF COLD FUSION IN A MITOCHONDRION

Let's assume that the daily required energy for an average person is 2000 kcal (one nutritional cal is equivalent to one kcal). The efficiency of the respiratory mitochondrion metabolism is estimated to be about 40%.[2] This means that about 40% of 2000 kcal, i.e. about 800 kcal, is spent for the production of ATP.[2] In section four we discussed that the kinetic energy of five out of each six H^+ ions is released into the matrix before it is absorbed by the enzymes FMN and Q. This kinetic energy is part of the energy produced from the breakdown of carbohydrates. Additionally, we noted that in order for the two protons to synthesize an ATP, each need to have a kinetic energy of about 1.45 eV. This energy is 1.23 eV more than the energy each proton gains through the inner membrane EPD (i.e., 0.22 eV). Consequently, the ionization energy of the bound hydrogen atoms (the energy necessary to push the protons against the 0.22 eV EPD and synthesize the ATP) should be provided by fusion. Let us assume that all of the energy needed for the synthesis of ATP is provided by fusion, making this the only consumed part of the energy produced by fusion. Therefore, the energy of the carbohydrate breakdown is not used for the ATP synthesis. This assumption does not invalidate the greater importance of the carbohydrate breakdown. It merely says that carbohydrates (food) are necessary for providing the mitochondrion with hydrogen or the fuel that is needed for fusion. On the other hand, fusion is necessary to provide the protons with enough kinetic energy to cross the inner membrane and eventually produce ATP. Accordingly, this assumption gives an equal importance to both food and fusion for life maintenance.

Let's assume a 1000 kcal/day is provided by fusion in an average size body, for example. In this case, the amount of energy produced in one second (or the power produced) is 48.4 W. As mentioned earlier, the average energy released by the fusion of two D nuclei is 8.3 MeV. Hence, there must be as many as $f = (48.4 \text{ W} / 8.3 \text{ MeV}) = 3.64 \text{X} 10^{13}$ fusions/sec occurring in an average size body. Taking the average diameter of an animal cell as 20 micrometers[2] and the average density of the cell as 1.72 g/cm^3 [15], we estimate the average number of cells in the body to be about 1.2×10^{12}. With this estimation, we are also assuming the average body mass to be around 70 kg. If we consider the average number of mitochondria in a cell to be 100, we then estimate the total number of mitochondria in an average body to be 1.2×10^{14}. Comparing this number with the frequency of fusion's needed in the body ($f = 3.64 \times 10^{13}$ fusion's/sec), we conclude that on the average we should have one fusion per mitochondrion each second.

In section eight we mentioned that the number of hard component cosmic rays is about $200/m^2$. sec. If we assume that the surface area of an average body as $1.2 \ m^2$, then the approximate number of muons that an average body receives is 240/sec. Since the least energy the muons contain is 2GeV, and the energy needed for each fusion is 0.29 MeV, then each muon ideally produces about 690 fusions. Thus, as many as $690 \times 240 = 1.656 \times 10^5$/sec. fusions are the result of the incoming muons themselves. Using f ($= 3.64 \times 10^{13}$ fusions/sec) needed in the body, we conclude that each produced neutron by muon catalyzed fusion should itself cause about 2.2×10^8 ($= 3.64 \times 10^{13} / 1.656 \times 10^5$) fusions/sec. Assuming that this fusion is a chain reaction, (i.e., each neutron product of the fusion produces two new neutrons through catalizing each fusion; $2^{28} = 2.68 \times 10^8$) this frequency of fusions ($f = 3.64 \times 10^{13}$ fusions/sec) can be obtained if each produced neutron goes through a maximum of 28 fusions. In essence, each muon should bring about a tree of fusion that at most branches 28 times (29 times totally). The average energy produced in a fusion is 8.3 MeV. Dividing this energy by that needed for the fusion of two D nuclei or a D and a T nuclei, i.e., 0.29 MeV, we obtain 28.6. This (28.6) is the average number of fusions that a neutron product of a muon catalyzed fusion can cause; and it is amazingly the same amount (28) needed. Hence, it is reasonable to conclude that 48.4 W can be produced by fusion in the body.

One of the ways to check the occurrence of fusion is to check the rate of neutron production in the system or neutron counting. The average number of fusion produced neutrons for each watt of power is 1.42×10^{12}.[16] With a power value of 48.4 W, we can expect the number of resulting neutrons per second to be 6.87×10^{13}. One may wonder why do we not see nearly as many neutrons ejecting from our bodies. There is an explanation for this circumstance.

As calculated earlier, the expected frequency of f = $3.64X10^{13}$ fusions per second in the average human body translates into one fusion per second in each mitochondrion. **It is my belief that hydrogen atoms or protons in the proton pool of the mitochondrion, absorb the neutron byproducts of these fusions and form a D atom or D nuclei.** This absorption takes place mainly because there is a reservoir of H and H^+ in the mitochondrion.

Another product of fusion is Helium. Assuming each fusion in the body produces one He, then the number of He atoms produced in the body will be $3.64X10^{13}$ per second. Taking the life span of a person to be 100 years, then the number of the He atoms produced through fusion in the body during our whole lifetime will be about $1.15 X 10^{23}$. This is equivalent to 0.19 mol of He atoms. Considering equal amounts of ^{3}He and ^{4}He in the body, the 0.19 mole of He is equivalent to 0.661 grams of He produced in one's body during his /her lifetime. Taking one's mass to be 70 kg, then the mass ratio of He by the end of one's life would be $9.44X10^{-4}$%. Taking into account the fact that air contains $5.24X10^{-4}$% He by volume, the above percentage[17] is certainly within the normal and acceptable range.

10 - PROFESSOR SADEGH ANGHA'S DIRECTIONS TO THIS WORK

In his book, <u>The Hidden Angles of Life,</u>[18] my father, Professor Sadegh Angha, states: *"In order to solve the puzzle of life, first we need to find the functional similarity of the forces acting in hydrogen in our bodies and those responsible for the sun's radiation..."* The forces responsible for the sun's radiation are nuclear fusion forces.[14] In fact, it has been known that fusion of nuclei less massive than iron result in a surplus of energy.[10] However, the fusion of the D nucleus with a T nucleus is the most efficient of all fusions.[14] Each second four million tons of mass in the sun are converted to the kinetic energy of He and neutrons as a result of the conversion of 657 million tons of H into 653 million tons of a mixture of He and neutrons.[10] The kinetic energy of the He and the neutron is responsible for heating the sun and consequently producing its radiation.

Later he predicts spectacular achievements in bioengineering and he says, *"The sole way to these achievements is the experimental investigation and subsequent discovery of all kinds of radiation and energies in our environment as well as their relations with our body's chemicals and cells.* "[18]

In subsequent pages he says "... *we are heedless of the great effect of the cosmic rays, the solar, planar, and all of the other gravitational fields, both on the very existence of the cell and its present cycle. Therefore, it seems to me that instead of spending all of our time merely investigating the cellular structure, we should first put our effort into building an apparatus that could analyze cosmic and ultra-cosmic rays. Then, study the effect of each of these radiations separately on the cellular cycle and the living state. Through this method, I am certain we will find more effective ways to correct the mistakes of the cellular life cycle in its fight against cancer or other similar diseases. We should pay more attention to the energy stored in the hydrogen atom. This energy is a deposit that a simple atom has carried within itself during its cosmic journey, ever since it was formed. I am confident that we will find the origin of life in the H atom or its compounds. Our cells are basically composed of four compounds of H atom. Under the influence of cosmic rays and their energy fields, the stored energy in these compounds is constantly being traded between the internal and the external part of the cell. This exchange of energy is the very agent of life on Earth. Consequently, without knowledge of this energy deposit and its relation to cosmic radiation, we will be unable to discover the origin of cellular life."*[18]

Obviously, by pointing out the importance of the effect of cosmic rays on cells and the understanding the hidden energy within the H atom, Professor Sadegh Angha is directing our attention to fusion in cells, especially when he mentions the fact that we should pay attention to the similarity of the forces acting in the sun and those acting in our cells.

11 - SUMMARY AND CONCLUSIONS

I have discussed the contribution of muon catalyzed fusion in ATP synthesis in a mitochondrion. Mitchell's theory explains the processes by which ATP is generated in the mitochondria. However, it overlooks the source of energy responsible for the—proton transport from the matrix to the intermembrane space of the mitochondrion. It also misses the fact that in order to synthesize ATP, the protons channeling through the F_0-F_1 enzyme need far more energy than the amount gained through EPD between the matrix and its outside. I discussed the fact that in the intermembrane space protons gain a drift velocity similar to the one gained by electrons during the process of electrical conduction through a wire. This drift velocity is a result of the difference in the proton population between the matrix and the intermembrane space. However, the protons have a thermal velocity that they acquire as a result of cold fusion in the mitochondrion. This thermal kinetic energy is responsible for driving the protons to the outside of the matrix to eventually synthesize ATP.

The energy gained through the breakdown of carbohydrates would be more than enough for ATP synthesis if all of it were transferable. However, in the respiratory cycle, most of the protons that carry the carbohydrate breakdown energy are released in the matrix where they lose their energy to the environment. This concurs with the fact that during the respiratory cycle the FMN takes one proton from NADH and another proton from the matrix. Similarly, the two Q molecules take their protons from the matrix. It is evident that these protons already have released their energy into the matrix since the average thermal energy of the molecules is much smaller inside the matrix. More importantly, the two protons which synthesize ATP need to have far more energy than that gained through the EPD between the inside and outside of the inner membrane.

Our body is constantly being bombarded by elementary particles from cosmic radiation. The main constituent of cosmic radiation at sea level is the particle muon. These muons catalyze the fusion of the D nuclei whose abundance is 1/6000 of that of H.

If fusion is responsible for ATP generation in the mitochondria, then there has to be approximately one fusion per second in each mitochondrion in our body. This is possible if the primary neutrons yield more fusions while they lose their kinetic energy to the atoms they collide with. Then they are more likely to have a final inelastic collision (be captured) with H atoms, protons, or a D to form a D or T. This marks the end of the chain of fusion reactions started by a muon.

Understanding fusion and the parameters influencing its function in mitochondrion will indeed prove to be very fruitful to us in the treatment of cancer and other diseases. My father Professor Sadegh Angha says: *"I wish I could assure the scientific community that the gateway to the discovery of the origin of the cellular living state is understanding the individual and collective radiation fields of the cells and their interaction with all of the cosmic radiation."*[18]

CHAPTER 2

FUSION IN PULMONARY, RESPIRATORY, AND OTHER SYSTEMS OF THE BODY

12 - ACTIVATION ENERGY AND ENZYMES.

All chemical reactions, even those which eventually release energy, need some energy in order to take place at all. The energy needed to activate a reaction is called activation energy. In the case of Adenosine TriPhosphate (ATP), where its hydrolysis results in Adenosine DiPhosphate (ADP) and inorganic phosphorous (Pi), the activation energy is 42 kJ/mol.[1,2] The net energy released as a result of this hydrolysis is 31 kJ/mol. Thus the ATP activation energy is greater than the amount the free energy produced.[1,2]

Below is a demonstration of how the value of the free energy of activation (δG) is derived. The equation for the δG is as follows:[2]

$$\delta G = RT \ln \frac{[\text{products}]_{pr}}{[\text{reactants}]_{pr}} - RT \ln K, \qquad (1)$$

where R = 8.31 J/mol.K is the gas constant, T = 300K is the absolute room temperature, $[X]_{pr}$ is the prevailing concentration of X in moles per liter, and $K = \dfrac{[\text{products}]_{eq}}{[\text{reactants}]_{eq}}$ is the equilibrium constant, with $[X]_{eq}$ being the equlibrium concentration of X in moles per liter.[2,3] From Arrhenius' equation we have $RT \ln K = \delta G^{\ddagger}$. Taking $\Gamma = \dfrac{[\text{products}]_{eq}}{[\text{reactants}]_{eq}}$ we have

$$\delta G = RT \ln \Gamma + \delta G^{\ddagger}. \qquad (2)$$

For ATP hydrolysis $\delta G = 73-31 = 42$ kJ/mol.[2] Using Avagadro's number ($N = 6.022 \times 10^{23}$ mol^{-1}) this free energy is equivalent to 6.92×10^{-20} J/molecule. Assuming this energy is due to the thermal energy of the molecules, i.e., $\delta G = 3kT/2$, we have $6.92 \times 10^{-20} = 1.5 \times 1.38 \times 10^{-23}$ T which results in T = 3400K. Obviously this is an impossibly high temperature to exist within our bodies.

An increase in the temperature of a solution results in an increase in the rate of molecular activity. After all, the magnitude of the temperature is an indication of the average kinetic energy of the molecules present in the solution.

Furthermore, in any solution there are molecules with much higher kinetic energy than the average kinetic energy within the solution. These molecules may be responsible for breaking through the activation energy barrier and inducing the reaction. An increase in temperature results in a greater number of these fast molecules and consequently a higher rate of reaction.

In order to reduce the relatively high average kinetic energy necessary for molecules to activate, living systems have developed enzymes as catalysts. In general, a catalyst brings the potentially reactive portions of adjacent molecules into closer proximity in order to promote reactivity. That is to say, a catalyst brings the reactant molecules to an *order* favorable to the reaction, thereby enhancing the rate of reaction. In essence, because the enzyme brings about a molecular order conducive to reaction, the activation energy needed for the reaction to take place is "reduced" considerably.

The chemical structure of a catalyst, however, is not permanently changed by a reaction, nor is a catalyst consumed during reaction. Enzymes are organic (protein) catalysts, and they contain a characteristic cluster of amino acids, called the active site. This is true of every enzyme, regardless of its chemical structure or the reaction it catalyzes. This active site is the site where the reacting molecules reside and are brought to order with respect to other neighboring molecules involved in the reaction. The active site is a cavity having its own characteristic energy structure. Molecules which actually undergo reactions are called the substrate, and the results of the reaction are called the products.[2]

Generally speaking, proteins are composed of 20 different amino acids.[2] Of these amino acids, only a few are involved in the active sites of enzymes. These acids participate in binding the substrate to the active site during the process of catalysis. *The proteins in the active site are donors or acceptors of protons. This proton exchange is the means by which the active site promotes the necessary order within the reacting molecule ensemble.*

Most enzymes are sensitive to temperature. In essence, an increase in temperature promotes the rate of enzyme catalysis. This increase however, is not indefinite. Beyond a critical temperature enzyme activity decreases, as does the reaction rate. This is primarily because the collisions do in fact change the chemical structure of the enzyme and the active site.

In addition to temperature, enzymes are sensitive to the pH of the environment.[2,3] In this case also, there is a critical pH level at which enzyme activity peaks and beyond or below which activity drops. The optimum pH for most enzymes is 6.5 - 7.5.[2]

Enzymes enhance the rate of reaction typically by a factor of 10^8 to 10^{10} compared to the uncatalyzed case. The initial contact of the substrate with the active site of the enzyme takes place through random collisions which result in the substrate binding to the enzyme. The binding of the substrate to the active site is that of hydrogen or ionic bond. The bond strength between an enzyme and a substrate molecule is usually between 12.5 to 50 kJ/mol.[1,2]

Enzymes activate the substrate by means of accepting or donating protons. This exchange of protons is believed to be one explanation for the relationship between enzyme activity and pH levels.[1,2]

The primary function of an enzyme, then, is to absorb the specific substrate and establish a molecular *order* favorable to the intended chemical reaction. We can treat the absorption part as an inelastic collision between the enzyme and the substrate molecules. In this kind of collision, part of the substrate's kinetic energy converts to heat which increases the entropy, S of the enzyme-substrate system and/or its temperature T. Establishing the subsequent order and bringing the substrate molecules to the active sites, implies a necessary expenditure of more work (energy) by the enzyme ensemble (molecules). Thus, the fact that the enzyme takes the substrate molecules and positions them in its active sites in such a manner that the appropriate surfaces are juxtaposed, implies a flow of energy into the substrate system. After the substrate molecules are bonded to the active sites of the enzymes, the substrate system is ordered and consequently less energy is needed to make the reaction take place. Based on this it is my belief that enzymes do not in fact reduce the activation energy needed for a reaction. *Instead enzymes give part of the activation energy to the substrate by bringing the captured molecules of the substrate into an* <u>*order*</u> *favorable to* *the reaction, and thus <u>orient</u> them for the reaction.* In this manner the energy that must be put into the system is reduced because a portion of it is provided by the enzyme. In essence, the stepwise flow of activation energy (in the presence of enzymes) has confused biologists into thinking that somehow the same reaction requires less energy when the enzyme is present. It is my belief that the total activation energy is the same whether an enzyme is present or not; only the form and the stages of the energy flow into the reacting substrate molecules differ.

Having established this position, the question then arises: What is the source which supplies enzymes with the energy they transfer to the substrate? The enzyme, as previously discussed, invests energy into the substrate, arranging and ordering the molecules in such a way as to predispose them to the intended chemical reaction. This is a repetitive process requiring energy on a continuous basis. The question then remains: Where does the energy needed for this function of the enzyme come from?

At this point we must remember that enzymes are composed of proteins, including all 20 amino acids.[2] On the average, 55 percent of the atoms present in amino acids are H

atoms (H^+ ions).[2] Therefore, comparatively speaking, there is

a much larger number of H atoms present in an enzyme than

in the substrate(e.g., ATP) or (generally) other molecules in

the environment.   Additionally, the large molecular mass

number of proteins (about 50,000) contributes to the

abundance of H atoms in enzymes. Considering these facts, I

believe that enzymes are either the very sites where cold

fusion of the H^+, or D, or T ions with the other H^+ ions or D

nuclei takes place or, alternatively, they (enzymes) are the

main recipients of the energy of cold fusion. Furthermore, it

is my contention that cold fusion provides energy to the

enzyme, enabling it to elicit from the substrate ensemble the

molecular order favorable to reaction.

In this fashion the enzyme supplies part of the

activation energy of the reaction to the substrate molecules.

Therefore, the enzyme-assisted hydrolysis of ATP is actually

facilitated by cold fusion.   Whether fusion occurs in the

enzyme or not, the energy of the fusion (which manifests as

the kinetic energy of the molecules of the environment) is

transferred to the enzyme by the H^+ ions. Because these ions are the lightest particles present (other than electrons), they are the transporters of kinetic energy in the environment. Since enzymes are composed of hydrogen-rich molecules (proteins), they attract fusion energy. The kinetic energy gained by the enzyme in this manner is partially transferred to the substrate molecules; thus giving them more mobility resulting in the increased possibility of favorable juxtaposition of their appropriate surfaces. The active site of the enzyme is where the substrate molecules receive this kinetic energy.

As the temperature of the environment rises, the number of collisions increases, thereby accelerating the rate of energy (produced by fusion) transformation. This enhances enzyme activity in the sense that the active site is energized more frequently and thus transfers energy to the substrate more rapidly. This process in turn speeds up the ordering of the substrate molecules. At very high temperatures, however, the enzymes decompose and the random motion of the substrate molecules is so great that the energy of fusion cannot establish the appropriate order.

The pH dependence of enzyme activity can also be related to the rate of fusion in the enzyme. At higher concentrations of H^+ ions in the environment (i.e., outside of the enzyme), the rate of fusion in the enzyme decreases because there are relatively more fusions occurring in the enriched H^+ environment.

On the other hand, since the system is in thermal equilibrium, the kinetic energy of the H^+ ions is on the average equal to that of the enzyme molecules. Since the enzyme molecule is at least 50,000 times more massive than a single H^+ ion, $M_{enz}/m_p = 50,000$, then from the equation $m_p v_p^2/2 = M_{enz}v_{enz}^2/2$, we have $v_p = 220v_{enz}$. Thus the protons are 220 times faster than the enzyme molecules. Consequently, the kinetic energy is carried around by the H^+ ions. In light of this, it becomes apparent that if the total number of protons decreases below a critical value, then the actual number of energy carriers decreases, thereby diminishing the overall activity of the enzyme.

In cases of enzyme inhibition, therapeutic treatment should consist of accelerating the rate of fusion in the body especially in the enzymes. This can be accomplished by limited bombardment of the body, with muon particles. A dosage of muon particles accelerates the rate of cold fusion in areas where there are clusters of H^+ ions, e.g., enzymes. The "extra" energy produced in the enzyme as a result of cold fusion facilitates and increases its activity which in turn lessens enzyme inhibition caused by agents such as drugs or poisons.

The inevitable influence of cold fusion on enzyme activity has been overlooked by bioscientists. Here again, careful and controlled experimental study of the behavior of enzyme activity as a function of the rate of cold fusion should prove beneficial.

13 - NERVE CELLS

There are two types of excitable cells in our bodies: nerve cells which transmit an electrical impulse, i.e., an electric current, and muscle cells which change their physical shape (contract or expand) as a response to electrical stimuli. The electrical properties of the cell membrane of these excitable cells changes in response to stimuli.[2,4]

The cells which form the nervous system and function as a response to stimuli are called neurons. On the average, a person's body contains 10^{10} neurons. The neuron contains the usual intercellular organelles including *mitochondria*. Figure 1 shows a typical neuron. The body of a neuron is called the soma. The axons and the dendrites connect to the soma. A neuron connects to other neurons via dendrites which furnish a large (up to 0.25 mm^2) area. Through this contact area the dendrites receive electric pulses from other neurons and transmit them to the soma. The axons carry the signals from the soma to the other neurons, muscle cells, and gland cells. The axon splits and swells up at its head, called the synaptic knob (terminal button). It is the synaptic knob of the axon which makes contact with the somas, dendrites, or the axons of the other neurons and conducts electrical signals to them. There are thousands of these contact sites on a single neuron covering up to 40% of the surface of the neuron.[4]

The cell membrane of the soma extends along the axon and is called the axolema. In the peripheral nervous system the axon is surrounded by the "shownn" cells.[4] In some neurons the shownn cells envelope the axon in multiple concentric layers to form the myelin sheath. This layer serves as insulation for ion currents.[4]

The synapse or synaptic knob is the area where signals are transmitted from the axon of one neuron to the dendrite or soma of another neuron, muscle cell, or gland cell. In mammalian neurons there is no actual contact at the synapse. The synaptic cleft (10 to 40 nano meter) separates the two neurons and acts as an insulator for transmission of a signal. The electrical signal that reaches the synapse releases a chemical transducer, the neuro-transmitter, into the synaptic cleft. The transmitter frees itself from presynaptic vesicles, diffuses to the postsynaptic membrane, and initiates a new electrical signal.[4]

An electric potential difference can be recorded across the membrane of living cells. According to cell type, the resting membrane potential amounts to 50-100 mV. (the cell interior is negative) in muscle and nerve cells.[4]

The actual number of ions across the living cell membrane differs. This introduces an electric potential difference across the cell membrane. This, as mentioned earlier, amounts to 50-100 mV, depending on the cell type. Any living cell exhibits this membrane potential but the excitable nerve and muscle cells have the ability to alter their membrane permeability leading to *a rather large range* of membrane potential.[4] An electrical stimulus produces transient changes in the ion conductance (thus the potential) of the excitable cell membrane. If the magnitude of the stimulus electric potential exceeds a critical value, then an electric current is transmitted along the nerve cell. In muscle cells this leads to contraction. The mechanism of the operation of the action potential is as follows. The positive electric potential of the stimulus disturbs the 50-100 mV electric potential difference across the membrane. This extra potential makes the outside potential more positive with respect to the inner membrane. At a critical potential difference called the threshold potential, the membrane conductance to Na^+ increases and the Na^+ channels become activated in order to maintain the 50-100 mV potential difference. There will then be a sudden influx of Na^+. The ion influx does not stop at the potential difference of 50-100 mV; rather, Na^+ ions keep flowing in to such an extent that the inner membrane may become electrically positive with respect to the outer membrane. However, before this happens, the membrane Na^+ conductance starts to decrease and the K^+ outflux membrane conductance begins to increase. This eventually leads to the re-establishment of the membrane potential of 50-100 mV. This is called the depolarization process.[4]

For a brief period following the depolarization phase, the nerve or muscle cannot be excited by even the strongest stimulus. This is the absolute refractory period and is succeeded by a relative refractory period (at the end of the repolarization phase) during which an action potential of a lower amplitude can be elicited, but only by a stimulus greater than the initial threshold stimulus. As the membrane potential returns to its original state, the threshold stimulus and the amplitude of action potential also return to their original value.[4]

The most important factor in the transmission of the signal through the nerve and muscle cells is the random motion (in contrast to drift motion) of the ions in these cells. Similar to electrical conductors (i.e., wires),[5] the ions inside the nerve cell have a thermal (random) motion as well as a net drift motion. As I have hypothesized, this random motion is due to the kinetic energy gained through fusion of the H nuclei (roughly one fusion per mitochondrion per second, chapter 1). Any action potential gives a drift velocity to the ions. The presence of fusion is necessary in order to provide for the random motion of the ions. The decomposition of ATP can also accomplish this; but this decomposition is achieved by enzymes which gain energy through fusion. Therefore, either directly through the collisions, or indirectly through the decomposition of ATP, fusion is responsible for the random motion of the ions in the cells, including the nerve and muscle cells. The task of the electrical impulse is merely to stimulate the nerve or muscle cells and give a directional net component to the previously "random" motion of the ions. If the random motion does not exist, then the Na^+ and K^+ will practically be frozen. In that case the ions' influx or outflow occurs much more slowly than what we see in the body. This means that the stimuli will be transmitted across the nerve cells very slowly and thus the nervous system would not work nearly as rapidly as it does. The random motion of the ions is vital to the function of the nervous system and that itself is a result of cold fusion.

14 - Muscle Cells

The muscle cell is a fiber with a diameter of 10-100 μm and a length of about 20 cm. The cell membrane of the muscle cell is called the sarcolema. Among the substances inside the muscle cell are myofibrils, sarcoplasm (cytoplasm), lysosomes, fat droplets, and glycogen. Substances such as glycogen, glycolytic enzymes, Creatine Phosphate (CrP) and amino acids are dissolved in sarcoplasm. Muscle fibers contain hundreds of myofibrils. A myofibril is subdivided to sarcomeres and has an average length of 2.25 μm. Thick filaments (myosin) and thin filaments (actin) compose sarcomeres. A sarcomer lies between two Z-plates which are *protein* structures. In the vicinity of the Z-plates, actin filaments compose the sarcomere. This is called the I band. The region where actin and myosin filaments overlap is called the A band. The region of the sarcomere that only contains the myosin filaments is called the H band. The center of the sarcomere is called the M line.[4]

Figure 2 shows a myosin molecule. Each half of the double head of the molecule contains an ATP-ase (ATP-synthase). The attachment of the neck to the double head is jointlike, which allows the molecule to have a certain degree of movement. This ability to swivel makes it possible for the actin myosin complex (actomyosin) to slide along one another.[4]

The building block of the functional part of the skeletal muscle is the motor unit. It consists of a single motor neuron and the muscle fibers that it energizes. The number of muscle fibers that a single motor neuron innervates varies from 5 to more than 1000. The area of the motor neuron is split into many collaterals in order to supply energy to its muscle fibers which may be spread throughout the entire muscle.[4]

One type of motor unit is called the fast twitch unit. The other type is called the slow twitch unit. The slow twitch unit has a more active oxidative metabolism; that is, it has more capillaries and myoglobin acting as small but immediately accessible stores of O_2. Therefore, slow twitch units are more resistant to fatigue than fast twitch units. The existence of myoglobin for O_2 storage explains why these units are more resistant to fatigue. The availability of O_2

asserts the hydrolysis of ATP. More energy is released, resulting in less muscular fatigue.[4]

Muscles with relatively more motor units are considered to be more active. The frequency of the neural impulse determines the degree of tension in a motor unit. The more motor units a muscle has, the greater the tension developed in it. The number of motor units also determines how detailed the activity of the muscle is.[4]

Changing the electrical signal of the motor neuron to the mechanical energy of the contraction of the muscle is achieved through neuromuscular junction. The small sacs of the motor neuron ending (vesicles) contain neurotransmitter molecules of Acetylacholine (Ach).[2,4] The motor neuron discharges the particles (exocytosis) of Ach from its presynaptic membrane's active zone to its subsynaptic elongated fissure (cleft). Each vesicle contains a certain quantum number of Ach molecules. The postsynaptic folds of the muscle membrane are immediately adjacent to the active zone of the motor neuron with its Ach receptors. The reaction of Ach with the muscular receptors opens the Na^+ (and K^+) channels. The Na^+ flows inside the muscle cell for 0.2-1 ms.

One molecule of Ach can activate about 2000 Na^+ channels and the resulting ionic current is several nano Amperes, lasting a few milliseconds.[4]

Although single Ach quantized energy exchanges discharge spontaneously, this is insufficient to evoke muscle contraction. The actual contraction can only take place after the arrival of action potentials via the motor neuron. In fact, it is the action potential- transmitted through the motor neuron - that elicits muscle contraction. The action potential releases hundreds of Ach molecules at the ending of the motor neuron. As a result of this burst of Ach, the ionic (Na^+) current induced in the muscle cell fires an electric potential (muscular action potential) in the muscle cell and muscle contraction results. After this contraction, a rapid repolarization (the inner cell membrane becomes negative with respect to the outer membrane) follows.[4]

Thus, the motor neuron releases Ach at the motor endplate, inducing an endplate current (Na^+ and K^+) that spreads electrically to a limited extent. Upon the arrival of the action potential which releases large amount of Ach, a secondary action potential (Na^+ and K^+ current) is set off and spreads over the sarcolema of the entire muscle cell. This secondary current then follows through a system of transverse tubules perpendicular to the muscle called the T system.[2,4]

The secondary action potential is conducted through the T system and rapidly reaches the innermost part of the muscle fiber. The longitudinal tubules release Ca^{2+}. Exceeding the amount of Ca^{2+} concentration from a resting value of about 0.01 micro mol/l eventually results in muscular contraction.[4]

The shortening or contraction of the muscle is in fact a result of the myosin and actin filaments sliding over one another. The sliding of the filaments over each other takes place through the movement of the myosin heads. This increases the region of actin-myosin overlap. The molecule ATP is necessary for this sliding. The myosin heads possess ATP-ase enzymes and break down ATP to ADP and Pi.[2,4]

The Ca^{2+}, Mg^{2+} ions, ATP, and ATP-ase are among the most essential substances for muscle contraction. As previously discussed, the secondary action potential is transmitted throughout the muscle cell and sets the Ca^{2+} of the longitudinal tubuli free. This results in an increase of

1000 fold in the Ca^{2+} concentration in the muscle cell. This Ca^{2+} binds with troponins resulting in a loss of inhibition in the formation of the Actin-Myosin (A-M) complex. With the aid of the energy released by ATP hydrolysis the Ca^{2+} is pumped back into the longitudinal tubuli.[4]

Each of the two Myosin heads (M) also binds one ATP. Once the myosin heads bind to the actin (A), the actin activates the ATP-ase of the myosin head and the ATP's split up and release energy. As a result, the A-M-ADP-Pi complex is formed.[2,4]

Next Pi and then ADP dissociate from the complex. This process causes the myosin head to drop from an angle of 90° to 50° and finally to 45°. Subsequently, in the presence of ATP, myosin heads dissociate from the actin and again resume their initial angle of 90°. In the presence of high Ca^{2+} concentrations, actin and myosin bind again and the whole process repeats itself (up to about 50 times for full shortening of the muscle). The cycle does not proceed simultaneously in all of the muscle myosin heads. If it did, muscular contraction would be jerky. Although at any moment only part of the myosin heads are tilted, the total number is the same, thus ensuring smooth conscious contraction. When the intercellular Ca^{2+} drops below roughly 1 mmol/l, the sliding cycle is ended.[2,4]

The ATP hydrolysis directly provides the mechanical energy needed for muscle contraction. The resynthesis of ATP can take place in three different ways 1) Breakdown of Creatine Phosphate (CrP). 2) Anaerobic glycolysis, which is the breakdown of glycogen or glucose to lactic acid, and 3) Aerobic oxidation of glucose to CO_2.[2,4]

The high energy of the phosphate bond of CrP can transfer to ADP for the synthesis of ATP. The CrP reservoir of the muscle (25 mmol/g) increases the energy available for muscle contraction by a factor of 5 relative to that of the ATP reservoir (hydrolysis). After the CrP reservoir is exhausted (about 30 seconds), the anaerobic glycolysis begins. There is also a glycogen reservoir in the muscle. The muscle's glucose-6-phosphate breaks down this glycogen to lactic acid and produces 3 moles of ATP per 1 mole of glucose. This anaerobic production of ATP is also possible via the breakdown of blood glucose to lactic acid. In this case, the net gain of ATP is 2 mole of ATP per 1 mol of glucose, since in this case one mole of ATP is needed for phosphorilation of glucose. In light activity, after about 1 minute, the aerobic production of ATP substitutes for this. In heavy activity however, the aerobic production of ATP occurs simultaneously with this anaerobic process. After the produced lactic acid reaches its limit, the anaerobic production of ATP stops.[2,4,6] Consequently, *the long term energy of the muscle activity is provided by the hydrolysis of the aerobically synthesized ATP.*

As discussed by others[2], the aerobic synthesis of ATP from glucose can rapidly generate 36 moles of ATP per 1 mole of glucose. This rapid muscular metabolism indeed requires an overall increase in blood flow, cardiac performance, and respiration. These systems, however, take several minutes to reach their steady state rate of activity. Before this happens, the gap in ATP production is met in three ways: anaerobic energy production, consumption of the short-lived muscle oxygen reservoir (myoglobin), and extraction of oxygen from the blood. The limiting value of this highly efficient aerobic energy production in top athletes is about 370 watts.[6] This rate primarily depends on the rate of O_2 supply and the aerobic rate of glucose and fat breakdown. If this limit is exceeded, the rate of ATP production becomes smaller than the muscular rate of ATP consumption and thus fatigue results. At this point the activity has to be stopped. In the process of recovery the body replenishes its O_2 reservoir. This explains why the O_2 consumption during the period of recovery remains high. About 20 liters of O_2 must be stored in the body. In order to store this amount of O_2, however, the heart and the lungs themselves consume some O_2. Consequently, the amount of O_2 consumption during the recovery period is more than 20 liters. The glycogen and CrP-O_2 reserves are also replenished during the recovery period.[4]

As previously discussed, the "random" speed of the ions plays a major role in the conduction of the electrical signal throughout the body. Both anaerobic-aerobic synthesis of ATP and its hydrolysis are deeply dependent on the occurrence of cold fusion in the environment. Cold fusion in the body is in fact the main source of energy for muscular activity.

The consequences are enormous. The beating of the heart, the motion of blood through the veins and arteries, the expansion and contraction of the lungs, the digestive movement of the stomach, the gastrointestinal movement, and in general every movement of essential body organs originates with the occurrence of cold fusion of the H^+ or D ions with H^+, and D^+, and T ions deep inside the muscle cells. Even cellular motion itself (which basically stems from the kinetic energy of the molecules inside the cell) is a result of cold fusion inside the cell.

I mentioned that in heavy work or athletic activity the O_2 supply aerobically breaks down the molecules of glucose and fat. In weight loss my suggestion is that actually the fat molecules can be "burned" faster with an enhancement of the rate of cold fusion in the body. The enhancement of the rate of cold fusion increases the speed of ATP synthesis which in turn speeds up the breakdown of fat and thus a faster overall weight loss.

15 - THE IMMUNE SYSTEM

When a foreign substance enters the body, it encounters two methods of body defense. One method is when one type of white cells (called T lymphocytes) surround and then kill it. The second is when another type of white cells (called the B lymphocytes) produce the antibodies responsible for recognizing and eliminating such foreign substances. The first method is called the cell-mediated response, and the second method the humoral response.[2]

The T cells and B cells also eliminate - each in its own way - those body cells which have had their surface altered in some way by a foreign substance, often a virus. The T cells proliferate and differentiate into activated T cells when they encounter the foreign invaders or altered host cells. Macrophages are those white cells responsible for engulfing and removing the debris of the target cells.[2]

Both B cells and T cells develop from hematopoietic stem cells located in the hematopoietic tissue - mainly the liver in embryos and the bone marrow in adult organisms. Hematopoietic stem cells produce other types of blood cells.

The stem cells can result in different sets of progeny cells. The type of the cells produced depends on the particular tissue in which the stem cells differentiate. The blood stream brings B cells and T cells to peripheral lymphoid tissues such as the spleen, lymph nodes, or tonsils. The B cells and T cells do not encounter foreign antigens before residing in peripheral lymphoid tissues. Only after this point do B cells and T cells encounter the foreign antigens in the lymphatic system or the bloodstream.[2]

On their surface the B cell and T cell carry about 105 molecules which serve as antigen receptors. One lymphocyte (B cell or T cell), however, can respond to only one antigen. Thus all of these molecules act in the same manner in that they respond to only one antigen. The fact that the B cell and T cell can respond to a great variety of antigens means that the surface molecules have a great variety of specificity. In the human body there are about 10^{12} lymphocytes responding to 10^8-10^9 different types of antigens.[2]

The B cell and T cell can respond to a countless variety of different antigens. The model mechanism for this responsiveness, which is universally accepted, is called the

colonal selection theory. This model was first suggested by
N. K. Jerne et al. in the 1950's and the experimental results
support it.[2]

The main theme of colonal selection theory is that
once an antigen is detected by the receptors of a lymphocyte,
the lymphocyte proliferates and matures. Thus clones of
lymphocytes are produced; all having the same ancestor and
the same antigenic specificity.[2]

According to colonal selection theory the lymphocytes
display two differentiation phases. The first is the antigen-
independent differentiation where hematopoietic stem cells
differentiate to initially uncommitted cells. The second is
antigenic-dependent differentiation which results when a
lymphocyte binds to that particular antigen and then this
lymphocyte starts proliferating and differentiating into
effector cells.[2]

Antibodies constitute a class of *proteins* called
Immunoglobins (Ig). Immunoglobins constitute about 20% of
the total plasma protein in the blood. As stated previously,
about 55% of protein is composed of hydrogen atoms (or
hydrogen ions). The basic antibody molecule consists of four

polypeptide chains, two identical light chains and two identical heavy chains. The molecular mass of each light chain is 23000 and that of the heavy chain is 55000. Thus, in each antibody molecule there are about $2(12650 + 30250) = 85800$ hydrogen ions.

The B cells and T cells undergo a rapid proliferation and differentiation. In view of the fact that this process of proliferation and differentiation requires energy - the more energy available, the faster this process occurs , I claim that cold fusion is the most important factor in this process. After all, cold fusion increases the kinetic energy of the molecules in the environment and the more energy the molecules have, the faster the processes take place.

I also believe that since the antibodies are such hydrogen-rich molecules, the rate at which cold fusion occurs in them is much greater than in their environment - just as in the case of enzymes. The kinetic energy given to the antibodies by cold fusion is the energy with which the antibody works against the antigens - that is, seeking and binding to the antigen. In the case of the T cells, once again their energy mainly originates from cold fusion and with this energy made available to them, they detect and directly eliminate the antigen.

Generally speaking, the energy of the development of all processes (in the body) is mainly provided by cold fusion. The manner in which this energy is spent, however, is greatly dependent on the organ and ultimately on its structural genetic code. Specifically, the energy of the development of T cells and B cells out of hematopoietic stem cells and their subsequent differentiation, is provided by fusion. However, the specific program, i.e., the blueprint for their proliferation and differentiation, should be a genetic code embedded mainly in the tissues where the proliferation and differentiation takes place.

The enhancement of cold fusion through limited muon bombardment of the body, among other things, should increase the rate of the T cell and B cell proliferation and differentiation, especially in a patient whose body energy level has been depleted. Fusion provides the molecules with direct kinetic energy. This is similar to providing the system with 100% useable fuel rather than with a fuel (food) which the body first has to process in order to convert (only a small percentage) into a useable form.

16 - THE LUNGS

The lung and its microscopic structure is perhaps one of the most well understood organs of the body. The function of the lung cells is not merely to cover the surface of the tubes; rather, the cells have functions such as the secretion of substances like surfactant, an immunological substance. Another important role of the lung cells is metabolizing substances produced elsewhere. Thus the lungs are considered as a system of diverse functions.[6]

Figure 3 shows a schematic of the lungs. The conducting zone of the lungs is composed of *bronchi* and *bronchioles*. No exchange of gases occurs within this zone. The bronchi and bronchioles conduct gases from the *trachea* to where gas exchange actually occurs. The structure of bronchi is as follows: Bronchi are composed of two *primary bronchi* which divide into secondary or *lobar bronchi* as they progress into the lungs. The secondary bronchi then divide again into *tertiary* or *segmental bronchi* which finally divide into *terminal* or *subsegmental bronchi*. The bronchioles have a diameter of approximately 1 mm. The *alveoli* (the air cells of the lungs) are attached to the sides of terminal bronchioles. The walls of the lungs at these points are too thick to allow diffusion of gas across them. Furthermore, they are covered with elastic connective tissue which also impedes diffusion.[6]

The gas exchange takes place in the *transition* zone of the lungs. This zone consists of the final bronchiolar division called the *respiratory bronchioles* (fig. 3). The mixing area for alveolar gas, inspired gas, and dead space gas resides in this transitional zone. The transitional zone is called the *acinus*. The acinus contains the respiratory bronchioles, alveolar ducts and alveoli. The respiratory bronchioles occupy about 17.5% the conductive zone occupies about 2.5% and the respiratory zone about 60% of the total lung volume. The blood vessels, connective tissues and other tissues occupy the remaining 20% of the 5000cc total lung volume.[4,6]

The alveolar passageway may be compared to a long corridor and the *alveoli* (fig. 3) resemble rooms adjacent to each other on the sides of this corridor. The alveolar corridor ends in an *alveolar sac*. Here, in the alveolar sac, most gas exchange takes place. The vital process of gaseous exchange takes place only in the respiratory bronchioles and alveolar region of the lungs. Diffusion is responsible for air movement in these regions since the pressure gradient is not high enough to conduct a flow.[4,6]

The adjacent alveoli are connected through inter-alveolar *pores of kohn*. Thus, there is a mixing of air between neighboring alveoli, thereby dropping the pressure gradient in the alveoli.

There are at least two types of alveolar specific cell types. *Alveolar type I* cells comprise about 40% of the total number of the alveoli. *Alveolar type II* cells comprise the other 60%. The total number of alveoli in the two lungs is about 300 million. Thus, the number of type II cells is about 180 million. Within type II cells (among other things) there are plenty of *mitochondria*. These cells also contain the code for production of pulmonary surfactant which reduces the surface tension of the alveolar lining. In this secretion are several macro-molecules whose properties change surface tension as alveolar surface area changes during normal breathing. Alveolar type II cells can differentiate into type I cells. Type II cells are also the primary stem cells of the alveolar epithelium. They are able to multiply rapidly when oxidative or injurious agents penetrate this area.[4,6]

The job of keeping the alveoli clean and sterile is that of the *alveolar macrophage*. With plenty of *mitochondria*, when active, macrophages provide maintenance for a rapid rate of processing the ingested debris. An individual's resistance to lung infections is directly related to the number of properly functioning macrophages. Bone marrow is the birthplace of the alveolar macrophage. Phagocytosis is the ability of phagocytic cells to ingest and digest particles. Phagocytosis is an energy-dependent process. The alveolar macrophages have the highest metabolic rate of any phagocytic cell.[4,6]

The function of the lungs is not restricted to gas exchange. The lung has a multitude of functions other than gas exchange. *These functions can affect the physiology of every organ in the entire body.* One of the previously mentioned metabolic activities of the lung is the biosynthesis of surfactant. The lung is involved in both the synthesis and breakdown of such substance.[4,6]

The fibrous framework of the lung is called the *interstitium*. There are three types of fibers in this framework, each with its own physical and chemical characteristic properties, and different specific functions. The *elastic fibers* are most resilient and distensible. Following inspiration, the elastic fibers provide recoil forces to restore smaller airways and vessels to their resting state. *Collagen fibers* set and impose the limit of distensibility of the small vessels and alveoli. *Reticular fibers* are primarily found around the smaller blood vessels. These fibers are not very elastic. They prevent the capillary network from dilating excessively and promote optimum blood flow to a wide range of vessels rather than excessive flow to a few. The fibrous framework of the lung resembles a three dimensional elastic mesh. During inspiration the "mesh" expands and thus the tension increases and during expiration, when the "mesh" contracts, the tension decreases.[6]

The alveo-capillary membrane is the ultimate functional unit linking the pulmonary and cardiovascular systems. Let us now concentrate on the dynamics of achieving appropriate concentrations of O_2 and CO_2 in the pulmonary capillary blood.[6]

First the partial pressure of dissolved O_2 is lower than the atmospheric pressure, whereas that of CO_2 is higher. The natural tendency is for these gases to move from higher concentrations to lower concentration areas. The path of O_2 is from the atmosphere to the lungs and then finally to the tissues. Consequently, the path of CO_2 is from the tissues through the lungs and lastly into the atmosphere. Second, the flow of gases down the concentration gradient is achieved through diffusion. Third, the uneven ventilation of the lungs affects gas exchange with the pulmonary blood. Fourth, the uneven perfusion of blood through the lungs also reduces the efficiency of gas exchange. A more detailed explanation of each of these conditions follows.[6]

Partial Pressures[6]

The exchange of respiratory gases between the atmosphere and the bloodstream is achieved through breathing. In essence, there is a decreasing O_2 concentration from the external environment to the trachea to the alveolus to the arterial blood to the interstitial fluid to the metabolizing cell and finally, to *the mitochondrion*. This is sometimes referred to as the O_2 cascade. This concentration gradient ensures the flow of O_2 from the atmosphere into the tissue.

The direction of the decrease in CO_2 concentration is opposite, i.e., from the cell to the alveolus. Equilibrium between CO_2 and alveolar and lung capillary blood O_2 occurs very rapidly. There are three factors which can affect this equilibrium:

The first factor is called ventilation-perfusion mismatch. This occurs when all well perfused capillaries are not in contact with well-ventilated alveoli. The second factor is O_2/CO_2 mismatch. This means that a greater volume of O_2 is taken up by the blood than the volume of CO_2 removed from it except during vigorous exercise. Third, diffusion is the only way respiratory gases move across the alveocapillary membrane and not by any active secretory process. There is no active secretory process responsible for transporting respiratory gases.

Diffusion[6]

The ultimate purpose of breathing is to provide O_2 to

mitochondria for fuel metabolism. The motion of the gas

molecules from the environment of higher concentration to

that of lower concentration is called diffusion. The molecular

weight and its solubility determine how quickly the gas

molecules will move across the alveolocapillary membrane.

The diffusion link between alveolus and capillary

membrane is the essence of gas exchange. When calculating

the extent to which the optimum quantity of arterial O_2 (both

dissolved in the fluid portion of the blood and bound to

hemoglobin) can be maintained in the bloodstream, we should

realize the effect of several factors. The first factor is how

much O_2 is available for breathing. Secondly the extent of

O_2 remaining in the mixed venous blood after systemic

circulation is complete. This indicates how much O_2 is used,

and what the ongoing metabolic needs may be. The third

factor is the extent of matching of ventilation and perfusion.

The fourth is the pulmonary diffusing capacity, i.e., the ability

of the gases to exchange with blood. The diffusing capacity is

a measure of the ability of alveolar O_2 to exchange across the alveolocapillary membrane to reach the hemoglobin molecules within adjacent erythrocytes. Exercise can increase the diffusing ability of gases and disease lowers the diffusing capacity.

Ventilation[6]

Although ventilation satisfies metabolic needs, during normal ventilation the lungs are not uniformly ventilated. Disorders related to ventilation are as follows.

Dyspnea is a pattern of ventilation whereby breathing is difficult or labored. When ventilation is more rapid than normal but with normal depth, tachypnea occurs. The case of increased rate and depth of ventilation is called hyperpnea. In this case ventilation is within metabolic needs. When the ventilation rate and depth are increased in excess of metabolic needs, we say hyperventilation has occurred. In hyperventilation there is insufficient air for adequate gas exchange.

Because many capillaries are not fully functional, alveolar dead space occurs in the alveolar region. In this case gas delivery takes place but its exchange with blood does not actually occur. The distribution of the inspired air is non-uniform because of the anatomical complexity of the 300 million alveoli in the healthy lungs.

Perfusion[6]

Perfusion means passing or pouring of a fluid through spaces in order to supply a tissue with oxygen by injecting it into an artery. A good estimate of the pulmonary blood volume is about 0.5 to 1.0 liter. At any instant, only 70 mls of blood is in the pulmonary capillaries. The numerous pulmonary capillaries, with their surface convolutions, provide a rather large surface area for gas exchange.

On the other hand, some blood coursing through the lungs does not pass any alveoli. Thus this blood does not get the chance to become oxygenated and is called "shunted." That portion of the left cardiac output which does not contact ventilated alveoli and has not participated in gas exchange is called "shunted." Shunt is of two kinds - anatomic and capillary. The above is actually the anatomic shunt.

Consequently, the blood returns from these capillaries to the left heart without having gone through any pulmonary gas exchange. Just as ventilation in the lung is non-uniform, so perfusion is ordinarily non uniform. This non-uniformity can be a result of both natural and pathological causes. The actual gas exchange between alveoli and blood takes place only when ventilation and perfusion interface. Many ventilation/perfusion inequalities occur normally in healthy lungs, e.g. as a result of gravity and change in body position. The irregularities in the gravitational forces imposed by the positional changes are quickly and adequately compensated by the lungs in a healthy way.

A normal lung is an organ whose integrity depends on the gas tensions grouped around an equilibrium value. Deviations from this equilibrium value are of prime damaging effect in the function of a lung. The greater the deviation, the less efficient are the lungs. In fact, like every organ in the body, pulmonary pathologies may be related to the disturbances in the ventilation/ perfusion ratio.

17 - The Blood And Hemoglobin [2,4,6]

The blood flowing throughout our bodies contains plasma, a yellowish fluid. There are two general cell types in plasma, namely erythrocytes (red blood cells) and leukocytes (white blood cells). The viscosity of blood is about 5.5 times that of water, very close to that of sea water. The acidity of blood is kept well constant (pH around 7.4) with bicarbonates, phosphates, and proteins.

About 55% of the total volume of blood is composed of the fluid (plasma) part. Some of the substances in this fluid part are O_2, CO_2, H^+, and other ions from the dissociation of acids, bases, salts, proteins, and non-proteins. There are a wide variety of proteins contained in plasma covering a wide range of functions. The remaining (solid) part of the blood is composed of cells and cell debris.

Erythrocytes (red blood cells) are the means of gaseous transport for hemoglobin. The viscosity of blood would be much higher if hemoglobin were a part of plasma.

The higher viscosity of the blood would mean more required work for its transport. The viscosity of blood is minimized by the fact that hemoglobin is bound to erythrocytes. The mammalian erythrocytes do not have a nuclei (they cannot divide) yet are metabolically active. About 66% of the volume of erythrocytes is water and 33% is hemoglobin. They are primarily produced in the bone marrow of the vertebrae, sternum, ribs, and pelvis. Erythrocytes are the last link in a long chain of cell types which differentiate from original stem cells starting from the marrow. Although the mechanism for the maturation of the erythrocytes is not yet known, once the need for erythrocytes is increased, the process of maturation and differentiation is enhanced as well, meeting the increased need. The average lifetime of an erythrocyte is 120 days and the body produces about 3350 erythrocytes/kg.sec.

As mentioned above, 33% of an erythrocytes is hemoglobin. As hemoglobin is released into the plasma, it disintegrates into its two main ingredients heme and globin. The disintegration of heme results in iron atoms and biliverdin, which converts to bilirubin.[2] In this case, the iron is deposited in the liver and spleen for the synthesis of new hemoglobin.

The transport of O_2 or CO_2 also occurs chemically by means of their physical dissolution in the blood. The O_2 and CO_2 combine chemically with the hemoglobin of the erythrocytes. The whole system of O_2 transport can be divided into four major parts.

1. The lungs, with their alveoli, are the first part where O_2 enters.

2. The blood, with its hemoglobin, is where the O_2 diffuses or chemically binds.

3. The circulatory system with its capillaries, cardiac output, blood pressure and blood volume.

The tissue with its mitochondria where the O_2 is used to decompose the carbohydrates. Hemoglobin molecules can transport O_2 very well, because when compared with plasma, the hemoglobin capacity is very large. One hemoglobin molecule can carry four O_2 molecules. Furthermore the hemoglobin molecule can release O_2 at any time needed. A

Hemoglobin molecule can box load and unload O_2 quickly over the entire range of pressure of O_2 found in the tissue. Additionally, it can change its binding energy to O_2 in response to the body's changing demand for O_2. Hemoglobin molecules also have the ability to buffer (to deaden the shock of) the acidity of blood in healthy environments.

The amount of O_2 dissolved in the blood is much less than that needed by the metabolizing tissues. To meet the O_2 need of these tissues, hemoglobin serves as the reservoir for chemical binding of O_2. Hemoglobin also transports CO_2 and H^+ ions. Thus, it is also a device for controlling the acidity of blood. Hemoglobin has a high binding affinity for O_2. Most of the stored O_2 is chemically bound either to hemoglobin or to myoglobin,[2,4] (which also has a high affinity for O_2). This high affinity does not mean that in instances of need the O_2 is not released to the system. Rather, in such cases, the affinity of hemoglobin and myoglobin is reduced and O_2 is liberated into the system. In males about 98.5% of the total O_2 carried by blood is in the form of bound O_2. In females 98.2% of the O_2 is in the bound form.

Body tissue is extremely dependent upon O_2 supply. Muscle tissue can only survive 3 minutes after which its O_2 supply falls under the critical value. Brain tissue is even more dependent upon O_2 supply. The aerobic metabolism of the brain cells may be critically affected after less than 4 seconds of O_2 deprivation.

Tissue metabolism requires a substantial portion of the available blood O_2. Yet the hemoglobin molecules are still about 75% saturated. Since about 98.3% of the blood O_2 is transported by hemoglobin, the saturation of hemoglobin is the main parameter in evaluation of lung's oxygenating ability.

The hemoglobin molecule consists of four binding sites (heme), for O_2. Thus one mole of hemoglobin carries 4 moles of O_2. Once one O_2 is bound to the first heme group, the O_2 binding affinity of the other three heme groups increases. The O_2 binding affinity decreases with unloading of O_2 from hemoglobin. The shape of the hemoglobin molecule changes slightly due to the alternate forming and breaking of the salt bridges among the various parts of the hemoglobin molecule. It is as if the hemoglobin molecule

18 - FUSION IN THE LUNGS AND BLOOD

What is the source of energy (or work) for the expansion of the lungs during inspiration? Although some energy is pumped into the lungs during expiration, it can be shown that the net work done on the lungs for each respiration is not zero. Biologists assume that ATP hydrolysis is the source of energy for breathing. However I believe the main source of energy for the multitude of functions of the lungs is the muon-assisted fusion of the H^+ or D, or T nuclei. As shown in chapter one, the molecular kinetic energy resulting from fusion is far greater than that produced by ATP hydrolysis. The lungs contain at least 180 million alveolar type II cells within which, among other things, there is an abundance of mitochondria,[6] the presence of which guarantees the occurrence of cold fusion. The energy produced as a result of fusion manifests itself as the kinetic energy of the molecules existing in the environment. The type II alveoli and their abundant mitochondria are the ignition point of this energy. The increase in the molecular kinetic energy of the alveoli in part manifests itself as an increase in the internal temperature and pressure of the lungs. As a result of this increased kinetic energy, the epithelial surface extends and, consequently, the lungs expand. The ideal gas equation is $PV = nRT$ where P is the pressure, V is the volume, n is the number of moles, R (= 8.314 J/mol. K) is the gas constant, and T is the absolute temperature of the gas.[3] Obviously the change in the kinetic energy of the molecules presented in the alveoli changes P, V, and T disproportionately so that a change in "n" is inevitable. Because the lungs form an open system, the inflow of air changes "n" so that the equation holds.

The expansion of the alveoli and consequently that of the epithelial surface concludes with the intake of air into the lungs. In the process of "normal" inspiration-expiration the net work done by the lungs on the environment is 4.68×10^7 ergs/minute.[6] This amounts to 7.8×10^5 ergs/sec. About 65% of this work is done against the elastic inspiratory muscles and 35% is done against other frictional forces.[6] There are approximately 180 million type II alveolar cells each containing approximately 100 mitochondria and approximately one fusion per mitochondrion occurring per second, each producing an average of 8.3 MeV of energy. Thus the energy of cold fusion in alveolar type II cells can be calculated to be approximately $2.39X10^5$ ergs/sec. Considering that the total energy needed for respiration is $7.8X10^5$ ergs/sec, the order of magnitude for the two energies is the same. If, on the other hand, we take the average number of mitochondria in the alveolar type II cells to be 327, then the energy produced by fusion is $7.8X10^5$ ergs/sec, which is the same energy needed for respiration. Obviously, the muscle cells (which contain mitochondria) of the lungs are also a site of energy production for the expansion-contraction of the lungs.

The energy for the production of the surfactant could very well be provided by these fusions also. It is possible for the surfactant to decrease surface tension by speeding up its macromolecules and then transferring their speed (and momentum) to the surface molecules. This transfer of speed (or momentum) reduces the binding potential energy of the surface molecules, thus decreasing surface tension.

Similarly, fusion in the mitochondria of the macrophages is the main source of energy for the function of the macrophages which keep the alveoli clean and sterile. Fusion also supplies the energy for rapid ingestion of cell debris. Fusion is the source of energy for the proliferation of macrophages as well. As I mentioned before, an individual's resistance to lung infections is directly related to the number of properly functioning and circulating lung macrophages. Thus, the proper rate of fusion in the mitochondria of the macrophages is perhaps the most important parameter in prevention of lung infections. Macrophages which have the highest metabolic rate of ingesting and digesting bacteria must be supplied energy by fusion in their mitochondria.

As mentioned earlier, the diffusing capacity of O_2 and CO_2 across the link between the alveocapillary membrane and alveolus is the essence of the gas exchange. Generally, one important parameter in the diffusion of a gas from one place to the other is the magnitude of the gas molecular speed relative to that of the other molecules in the environment. Fusion provides kinetic energy for O_2 and CO_2 molecules, thus facilitating their diffusion. In general, as the kinetic energy of the molecules increases, the time they spend in the state of local binding to one another decreases; thus the diffusion rate increases.

As previously mentioned, the composition of blood very much resembles that of sea water.[6] In fact, one could say that blood is an evolved form of sea water. For example, species like sponges survive perfectly well by having sea water percolate inside them, thus allowing O_2 and nutrients to enter and CO_2 and wastes to exit the organism. In more advanced (animal) forms of life, blood takes the place of sea water in performing these functions and has evolved more highly developed functions as well.

To investigate fusion in the blood, the erythrocytes (red blood cells), leukocytes (white blood cells), and some cytoplasm bits called platelets are suspended in plasma. There are about 5.4×10^9 erythrocytes, 7×10^6 leukocytes, and 2.5×10^8 platelets in one cc of blood.[6] Since the erythrocytes do not contain mitochondria, the mitochondrial cold fusion does not take place in them. Taking the average number of mitochondria in the leukocytes as 100 and the rate of cold fusion as one per second per mitochondrion, then the approximate energy produced in one cc of blood is 9300 ergs$/$second. The main function of the erythrocytes is to carry hemoglobin, thereby minimizing the viscosity of the blood. If hemoglobin were carried by the plasma, the blood viscosity would be much higher, therefore requiring considerably more energy for circulation. Because the primary role of hemoglobin has long been assumed to be the transportation of O_2, its important role of H^+ transportation and containment has received much less attention.

Each minute metabolizing cells consume approximately 250 ml of O_2 and produce approximately 200 ml of CO_2. Plasma carries twice as much CO_2 as that carried by erythrocytes. The CO_2 metabolized by cells is carried either in a dissolved or a hydrated form; i.e., H_2CO_3 or combined with plasma proteins and hemoglobin. About 94% of CO_2 is carried in the bound or hydrated form. According to the equation

$$H_2O + CO_2 \longrightarrow H_2CO_3 \longrightarrow H^+ + HCO_3^-$$

carbonic acid dissociates to H^+ and HCO_3^-. Much of the H^+ produced from this dissociation of carbonic acid then bonds with hemoglobin and subsequently releases a K^+. However, I argue that cold fusion takes place in erythrocytes during the time when the H^+ is, in fact free.[6]

Thus, hemoglobin also carries H^+, which suggests the idea of fusion in hemoglobin itself. The changing affinity of hemoglobin for O_2 can be explained by the number of fusions in hemoglobin being related to the amount of H^+ ions. Thus, the more H^+ present in hemoglobin, the greater the number of fusions, resulting in more kinetic energy transferred to the particles present in the environment. Therefore, there will be a larger number of collisions with more energy exchange. This means O_2 molecules are separated from hemoglobin more frequently if more H^+ is present. Thus, the hetrotrophic behavior of O_2-hemoglobin could be attributed to fusion occurring in hemoglobin itself.

Consequently, in addition to the fusion energy produced in the mitochondria of the leukocytes, the presence

of H^+ in the erythrocytes produces additional fusion energy in
blood.

19 - MUON PRODUCTION IN WATER AND BLOOD

In chapter one I mentioned the fact that the primary cosmic ray - mainly containing protons - collides with the O_2 and N_2 in the atmosphere and produces π mesons which disintegrate to muons. We can produce muons by sending a fast moving beam of ions from a particle accelerator to collide with a sample of ordinary matter such as carbon.[7] In general, whenever protons collide with the nuclei of the atoms, they can produce muons. Natural examples of this are the production of muons in the upper atmosphere through the collision of the protons with the nuclei of O_2 and N_2 molecules.

On the other hand, looking at the molecular structure of water, we immediately notice that the conditions for the production of muons are all present. Notice that there are always some free O^- ions in water as well as some H^+. The main reason for the presence of these "fast protons" is that the muons which enter the water from the upper atmosphere catalyze fusion thereby giving kinetic energy to the environment. Obviously, the production of the secondary muons depends on the pH of the environment as well as on the number of free O^- ions.

The collision of the protons with the nucleus of the ions can also have the following result. The "fast proton" colliding with the nucleus of the O^- ion or O_2 molecule takes away one neutron (and possibly one proton) from the nucleus of the oxygen. The remaining nucleus resembles a nitrogen (N) more than an oxygen atom. The presence of the N in the environment makes it possible for the protons to collide with it and to knock off a proton and a neutron to produce the carbon nucleus. The presence of N and C in the environment makes possible the formation of CarboHydrates(CH) and consequently organic molecules.

The kinetic energy that a proton needs to penetrate the nucleus of an Oxygen or a Nitrogen can be calculated[5]

$$W = n(ke^2/r) \text{ J} \qquad \text{or } W = n(ke/r) \text{ eV} \quad (3)$$

where n ($\leq$ 8) is the number of protons in the Oxygen or Nitrogen nucleus, k = 9X10^9, Nm^2/kg^2 is the electrostatic constant, e = 1.6X10^{-19} Coulomb is the charge of the proton, and r = 2X10^{-15} m is the approximate radius of the O and N nuclei. Then W $\leq$ 8X1.44 = 11.32 MeV. Considering the fact that the average energy released in D-D fusion is 8.3 MeV, the energy to penetrate the nucleus of O or N is certainly available to some protons (which carry more than average fusion energy). However, this energy is not enough to produce a π meson which is the first particle produced when the proton collides with the atomic nuclei.

The lower energy end of the spectrum of the secondary cosmic ray (including muons) reaching the surface of the earth is 2 GeV. This means that among these particles, muons with energies as big as 2 GeV are not scarce. These muons can certainly result in fusion byproducts (neutrons) with kinetic energies bigger than 1 GeV. On the other hand, according to experimental results protons (or neutrons) with energies between 1 to 2 GeV have produced π mesons in their collision with other nucleons. The proton-neutron collision can be as follows:[8]

inorganic molecules) to environmental conditions. Perhaps the most important of these conditions is that the internal energy of the system naturally is preferred to be minimum. In a particular environment this (minimum internal energy condition) determines if the molecule formed is an organic or an inorganic one. Blood resembles the sea water. Blood like sea water contains an abundance of free H^+ ions, i.e., protons, O_2, N, and C. *The neutron byproducts of fusion in blood collide with the other nucleons and nuclei producing the secondary muons.* This explains why there can be a limited chain reaction for the production of the muons, providing an average of one fusion per mitochondrion per second. Since the O_2 molecules are transported ultimately to the mitochondrion, then the production of the secondary muons can indeed take place in the mitochondrion as well.

The production of the secondary muons in the H^+, O_2, N_2, and C reach the environment of the body and their subsequent catalysis of fusion, the source of life energy, is extremely important. Only by a careful investigation of this aspect of energy production can the search for the control of diseases be successful.

In his book <u>The Epic of Life,</u>[9] Professor Sadegh Angha assures us that the secret of life is embedded in water. He predicts that "the secret of life will be discovered in water - within sixty years from the date of his prediction – in the future." In <u>The Hidden Angles of Life,</u>[10] he explicitly indicates the primary importance of H^+ and O_2 in the conduction and preservation of "life". He defines life as a form of electromagnetic energy and says "water conducts life's electromagnetism."

To conclude, I contend that muon-catalyzed fusion is the source of energy for "life". Every system which can conduct the synthesis of muons and their subsequent catalysis of fusion should be considered as *"alive"*. From mitochondrian to muscle cells to proteins and enzymes to the proliferation of the B cells and T cells and to every other living system, the production of muons through the collision of H^+ ions with the nucleus of O_2 or C or N nuclei and their subsequent catalysis of fusion is the main ingredient of "life". In the same way that the viral form of life can and does indeed survive through direct p-p collision and their subsequent fusion in galactic space, muon-catalyzed fusion is the guardian of life on the surface of the earth. *Protons and O_2 are the messengers of life on the surface of the earth producing muons, i.e., the agents of life which catalyze fusion the guardian power of life.*

20 - On Medical Applications of Cold Fusion

The rate of cold fusion in cells and blood is determined by two factors. The first factor is the number of muons per second in cosmic rays bombarding the body, and the second is the pH level of the system itself. The pH level also determines the rate of muon production in the blood, or generally speaking, in the body itself. Unknowingly, traditional medicine has limited treatment for physical diseases where the pH level of diseased organs is manipulated to alter the rate of cold fusion. Medication prescribed by a traditional doctor changes the acidity of the blood, thus changing the concentration of H^+ ions in the entire body. This latter parameter changes the rate of secondary muon production as well as cold fusion, i.e., the energy level of the body. If the change is toward a more acidic environment (more H^+), then the rate of secondary muon production as well as fusion increases and more energy is produced in the body. The availability of more energy to the body results in , e.g., increased production of B and T cells, thereby strengthening the immune system of the body. Since this process makes more energy available to cells in the entire body, they reach maturity more rapidly and divide more often. The increased abundance of B and T cells, coupled with this accelerated rate of cell regeneration, enhances the body's ability to eliminate foreign organisms and damaged cells and replace these damaged cells with healthy new ones. This process continues until such foreign organisms are sufficiently weakened and diseased cells are eliminated and replaced. The body then returns to its original balanced state and the person is termed "cured." Traditional medicine can thus be considered as an attempt to control cold fusion in the body by means of the blood pH level manipulation and consequently that of the cells.

In order to fight some diseases, on the other hand, the body needs more energy or a higher rate of fusion than is available to it from this process (manipulation of the blood pH level) alone. In fact, it is logical to assert that for a fixed number of muons, the curve of fusion versus the number of the H^+ ions is asymptotic, i.e., it saturates beyond a certain number of H^+ ions. In this case no matter how much the number of H^+ ions or the pH of the environment is increased, the number of fusions in the cells is not going to increase. *Consequently some diseases, e.g., cancer and AIDS, cannot be cured merely by changing the pH level or administering medication.* To address this problem, modern medicine has turned to radiation therapy. Radiation therapy should attempt to manipulate the first parameter which controls cold fusion in the body, namely, the rate of muons bombarding the body per second. *However, since the wrong particles,e.g. photons, are used, the rate of fusion does not increase sufficiently to eliminate the disease.* Because of a lack of understanding of the occurrence and vitality of cold fusion in the entire body, traditional medicine has failed to use radiation therapy properly. Obviously, we can (and should) increase the rate of fusion by bombarding the body and, consequently, body cells, with simulated muons (section 12). Thus, my suggestion for a much less invasive and more rapid treatment of both internal and external injuries (next section) as well as other diseases is muon radiation therapy applied subsequent to administration of a medication which increases the pH level of the body.

As noted before, the structure and function of the immune system of the body is based on the proliferation and differentiation of the lymphocytes, i.e., B and T cells. This is the underlying idea behind the most widely accepted theory of the mechanism of the body's immune system, namely, the colonal selection theory. A characteristic deficiency in AIDS, however, is lymphopenia, a marked reduction in the number of lymphocytes in the blood.[2] This reduction manifests itself as a loss in the body's ability to maintain its immunity, hence becoming susceptible to a variety of diseases. In theory, reconstruction of the immune system would be an effective treatment.[2] That is to say, the body must regain its balance in the production of B and T cells.

My suggestion for this "reconstruction of the immune system" is the bombardment of those body parts responsible for the production and conduction of lymphocytes, i.e., the long bones, the thymus, the spleen, the tonsils, and the lymph nodes, with controlled high dosages of muons. This will enhance fusion at these sites, thereby facilitating proliferation of B and T cells, the lack of which is the symptom of AIDS.

I believe that rather than looking for a medicinal cure for AIDS, researchers should seriously and systematically study the effects of muon bombardment of the body. This is one of the many diseases which I believe can and will be cured through "muon radiation treatment method."

21 - THE INJURY REPAIR
MECHANISM AND FUSION

Injuries to the body can be divided into external and internal ones. In both types of injuries the mechanical damage is repaired by cellular substitution through fast cell division.[2] This rapid division of cells at the site of damage has been the source of consternation for immunology. What triggers the onset of fast cellular reproduction at the site of damage? To answer this question, let us look at energy production in the blood and the specific means by which this production is enhanced. In the last sections it was demonstrated that the source of energy in the erythrocytes is cold fusion of H^+ ions.

When an external injury occurs, the blood at the site of injury is exposed to the O_2 in the air. The mitochondria in the leukocytes are therefore exposed to larger amounts of O_2. This means that the rate of ATP generation in these mitochondria will accelerate, thus producing more H^+. This increase in the H^+ content of the mitochondria in turn increases the rate of cold fusion, which results in   more energy in the cell. The rate of energy production in the cell is related to its rate of maturity. In essence, the increase in the rate of energy production in the cell will enhance the growth of the cell. The leukocytes at the site of the injury grow, thereby accelerating the cell cycle. The same happens to body cells around the site of the injury, i.e., due to enhanced fusion they too grow faster and subsequently experience an accelerated cell cycle.

A similar case can be made for the repair mechanism of internal injuries. Because the leukocytes in this instance are not exposed to any extra amounts of O_2 from the air, their rate of growth and division remains unchanged. On the other hand, the interior cells of an injured internal organ will be exposed to more body fluids including more H_2O or H^+ + HO^-. I believe that cold fusion among these H^+ ions produces energy which is then transferred by means of collisions to exposed cells, thereby enhancing their growth and their division. Therefore, injuries can heal much more quickly when rapid fusion is induced at that location.

Experimental studies of the effects of cold fusion on the rate of repair and healing of injuries will indeed prove to itself were breathing, with oxygenation and deoxygenation alternately causing an expansion when O_2 binds and a contraction when O_2 leaves. During the lifetime of an erythrocyte, there are about 10^8 of such shifts.

The presence of CO_2 affects the interaction between hemoglobin and O_2. Interactions such as this where the presence of one molecule (CO_2) affects the binding of another (O_2) to the third molecule (hemoglobin) are called heterotrophic interactions. Thus the CO_2 entering the capillary blood of the tissues actually assists hemoglobin to unload O_2. Once CO_2 is removed from hemoglobin in the lungs, again the binding affinity of hemoglobin for O_2 increases; i.e., the removal of CO_2 facilitates the hemoglobin reoxygenation. This great affinity is reduced mainly by CO_2 and H^+ ions. By binding to hemoglobin, CO_2 and H^+ reduce the affinity of hemoglobin for O_2.

$$p + n \rightarrow p + p + \pi^-,$$

$$p + n \rightarrow p + p + \pi^- + \pi^0,$$

$$p + n \rightarrow p + n + \pi^- + \pi^+$$

Subsequently, in less than $1X10^{-7}$s, the $\pi^{\pm}$mesons decay to a muon and a neutrino $\pi^{\pm} \rightarrow \mu^{\pm} + \nu$, where ν is the particle neutrino (antineutrino). Therefore, the cosmic ray muons certainly have the capability to produce neutron fusion byproducts which result in the production of secondary muons themselves.

It is my belief that the production of muons in the "suds" of the sea water where there is an abundance of O_2 molecules and their subsequent catalysis of fusion is the main and the most influential parameter in the appearance of life on the surface of the earth. In fact, *life energy is nothing but fusion energy. Fusion is the very secret of life on the surface of the earth.* The energy of fusion increases the affinity of atoms for one another. Thus, *fusion catalyzes life.* We can attribute the production of organic molecules (in contrast with be very enlightening. Perhaps such studies will begin to pave the way for a "space age" medicine in which our "modern" surgical techniques are relegated to primitive technologies.

The effect of cold fusion on the rejuvenation of body organs and on the body as a whole also offers an avenue for careful investigation. I believe the primary difference between a "young" and an "old" organ lies in the rate of cold fusion taking place in each, the young organ having a higher rate of cold fusion than an old one. The effect of cold fusion on both internal and external injuries can be tested by exposing the injured organ to different dosages of laboratory produced muons.

22 - DEEP BREATHING

One very important factor in the treatment and healing of diseases is O_2. As discussed before, oxygen (O_2) is one of the main ingredients necessary to produce muons. The number of the produced muons is, among other things, dependent on the number of available O_2 molecules. Oxygen intake also increases the rate of cold fusion in body cells and thus enhances the energy production of the body. On the other hand, the most important factor which leads to disease is the lack of energy available to different systems in the body e.g., the centers with the erythrocytes. If there is enough energy available to the body and its individual systems, then among other things cell maturation and proliferation are accelerated, the rate of proliferation and differentiation of the B and T cells especially increases, resulting in the strengthening of the body's immune system. Therefore, in the presence of germs and viruses the body and its organs will indeed maintain their balance. The proper amount of O_2 supply is one of the crucial factors in disease control.

In normal breathing, about 0.5 liter of air enters the lungs. However, in deep breathing as much as five liters of air can enter the lungs, i.e., ten times as much.[6] This additional O_2 taken into the lungs and thus into the alveoli will increase the pressure of O_2 of the blood and saturate the hemoglobin. Thus, the entire body will receive considerably larger supplies of O_2. More muons are produced, and more carbohydrates are "burned" in the mitochondria of cells resulting in the release of more H^+ ions. The higher number of muons, along with the fact that the higher concentration of H^+ leads to a greater number of fusions in the mitochondria, result in raising the energy level of the body. Therefore, I consider *deep breathing* to be an important preventative factor in disease control and treatment.

Maintenance of a high fusion rate in the body is the best method of disease prevention. Deep breathing is one relatively simple mean of accomplishing this. Deep breathing is, of course, automatically done during exercise. It can be extrapolated that athletes indeed possess higher levels of immunity to disease due to their increased intake of O_2 and correspondingly accelerated rates of cold fusion. I would like to suggest that in conjunction with muon therapy, treatment of cancer and AIDS patients should include deep breathing sessions, using almost pure O_2. Such treatment incorporates the use of *two* factors which control fusion in the body.

A primary difference between deep breathing and exercise is that exercise generates more body heat. As previously discussed, thermal energy speeds up H^+ ions and increases the possibility of the occurrence of fusion. Exercise results in a more enhanced fusion than deep breathing alone. Consequently, exercise is more beneficial to the body than mere deep breathing.

23 - A New Method of Cancer Treatment

One of the diseases that human beings have not yet been able to successfully control and cure is cancer. Cancer is a disease characterized by uncontrolled cell proliferation. In the early 1920's Otto Warburg showed that the metabolism in cancerous cells is shifted towards fermentation.[2] Albert Szent-Gyorgyi says:[11] *Except for the most highly differentiated cells, such as those of the brain, animal cells have two states: the state of proliferation, and the state of rest. I have called these states the α and β states. The α state of proliferation is closely related to the state in which living systems existed before light and oxygen appeared. It makes all dividing cells similar to one another, and makes embryonic cells share many properties with the cancer cell. This proliferative state with its poor differentiation has higher entropy and lower free energy, which makes it the more stable state into which the cell tends to return. It is the ground state to which the cell will return when its organization is deranged. The cancer cell and the normal dividing cell differ mainly in their reversibility. The cancer cell is unable to rebuild its β state after it has completed its division and has to persist in its proliferative α state..."* He further explains the α state as follows: *"When life originated some three billion years ago, our globe must have been a very unpleasant place, hot and pitch dark, being surrounded by a very heavy layer of water vapor. There was no light and no oxygen. This stage of biological organization I termed the "α state." At this stage the main function of living systems must have been fermentation and proliferation. ...*

To be able to divide, the cell has to dismount its structure to a great extent ... ***Also the oxidative mitochondria have to be disassembled, making the cell more dependent on fermentation for energy.*** *All this means that the dividing cell has to differentiate and return, to an extent, to the α state. After completed division, the cell has to find its way back to the oxidative-resting β state."*

According to Szent-Gyorgyi, the α state has a more liquid structure whereas the β state contains extensive semisolid structure.*12* He also mentions: ***"We will understand cancer when we understand normal regulation,*** *and we will understand normal regulation, when we can describe it in terms of the basic parameters, energy, entropy, and quantum rules."*[13] He also discusses the fact that there is a lack of cohesive energy in cancerous cells.[14]

I believe what happens in a cell to make it cancerous is the following: A) The cell's respiratory cycle stops due to lack of fusion in the mitochondria causing the cell to revert to its fermentative state. B) As a result of the absence of fusion there is much less heat produced in the cell. The thermal motion of the molecules in the cell takes part in breaking off the water molecules. The lack of this thermal motion however, means that there is more water in cancerous cells. This explains why cancerous cells have less viscosity or smaller cohesive energy and also indeed have a bigger volume than normal cells. C) **The cell continues its ever proliferation in an attempt to regain its oxidative state. In fact, proliferation is the method that the cancerous cell adopts to fight the anomaly of lack of kinetic energy.** It is a cure that the cell applies time and time again without success. This lack of internal energy also causes the free energy of the cancerous cell to be lower than that of a normal cell.

In order to bring the cancerous cell back to its oxidative-resting β state, I believe we should facilitate fusion in the mitochondria of that cell. To achieve this goal I suggest the following: Instead of electromagnetic and other radiations, patients should be irradiated with muon beams. This would increase the rate of fusion in all of the patient's cells, including the cancerous ones. In addition, cancerous tissues should be exposed to O_2. The presence of O_2 in the mitochondrion leads to more oxidation of carbohydrates and this in turn increases the presence of H^+. Finally, the presence of muons and the abundance of H^+ in the mitochondrian will facilitate fusion. This fusion provides the energy necessary for the respiratory cycle and thus the cell regains its oxidative-resting β state and ceases proliferation, leading to the cure for cancer. My last suggestion is to increase the thermal energy of the cancerous cells. This can easily be done by the application of excessive local heat. One important effect of thermal energy on the cancereous cell is to evaporate the water it contains, or in general, increase the molecular "random" speed. As a result of this so called burning of the cell, there will be more ionization of H_2O molecules in the cell. This, along with an increase in collision rate, leads to an increase in abundance of both the H^+ ions and O_2 molecules, both of which lead to the enhancement of fusion in the cell. The evaporation of the cell water content also results in an increase in the cohesive energy of the cell and reduces its liquidity, i.e., the cell approaches the β state. Therefore, I recommend local burning of the cancerous tumors as a very effective preliminary method to bring the cancerous cells toward the β state, i.e., to cure cancer.

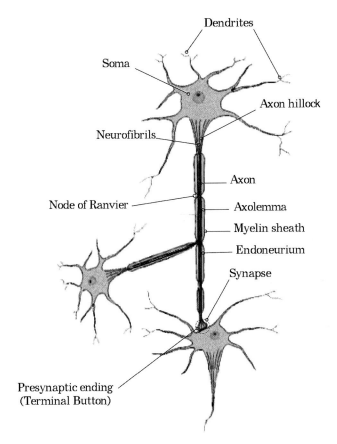

Figure 1- A schematic of a neuron. The body of a neuron is called the soma. A neuron connects to other neurons via dendrites which furnish a large area (up to 0.25 mm ^{2}). Through this contact area the dendriets receive electric pulses from other neurons and transmit them to the soma. The axons carry the signals from the soma to the other neurons, muscle cells, and gland cells.

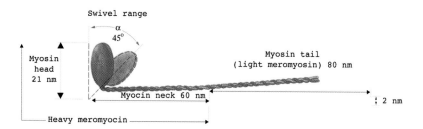

Figure 2 A schematic of a myosin molecule. Each half of the double head of the molecule contains an ATP-ase (ATP-synthase). The attachment of the neck to the double head is jointlike, which allows the molecule to have a certain degree of movement. This ability to swivel makes it possible for the actin myosin complexes (actomyosin) to slide along one another. (using figure C in ref. 1, page 35).

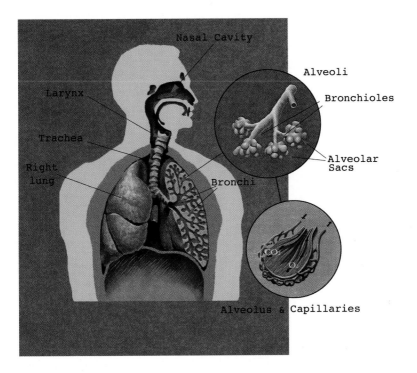

Figure 3. A schematic of the lungs. The bronchi and bronchioles conduct gases from the trachea to where gas exchange actually occurs. The bronchioles have a diameter of approximately 1 mm. the alveoli (the air cells of the lungs) are attached to the sides of terminal bronchioles.

CHAPTER 3

COSMIC BREATHING

24 - INTRODUCTION

In chapters one and two we investigated the mechanism of breathing, i.e., the intake of O_2 and the exit of CO_2, stating that ultimately breathing is accompanied by the fusion of H^+, D, and/or T nuclei. Inspiration results in the expansion of the system and expiration results in its contraction. Inspiration also results in fusion in mitochondria. The question then arises: "Can the fusion of two systems lead to the breathing of those systems?" In other words, are the expansion and contraction of systems equivalent to their fusion with each other? Can we generalize the concept of breathing to include those systems which experience a change in their total energy?

In this chapter we begin by discussing how the fusion of two H^+ or H^+-D (or, in general, any two nuclei lighter than iron (Fe)) results in the expansion of the "matter part"[1] of the component nuclei. The fusion of nuclei heavier than Fe results in the contraction of the "matter part"[1] of the fused nuclei.   Based on these assumptions and observations, *I define breathing as the fusion of two systems in nature.* I further generalize that regardless of the size of the attracting components, once they combine, their atoms expand as if they have inspired. Also I will talk about the breathing of molecules and more complex systems.

The gravitational attraction and subsequent union of the components of a planet (or a star) results in an increase in the penetration radius of the "matter part"[1] of the particles of the planet. I have termed this "gravitational breathing" and will discuss it in detail. I will also discuss the "breathing" of the sun both within this context and the context of fusion and talk about the gravitational breathing of the earth and the planets. Next I will investigate the inspiration of the universe, Professor Sadegh Angha's theory of this inspiration (or expansion) and simultaneously elaborate on the inside structure of the penetration sphere of particles.

I will explain the expansion of the "matter part"[1] of particles subsequent to their combination (thus building stronger fields) and their contraction after accelerating away from each other. Next, I will discuss Prof. Sadegh Angha's definition of "motion" and will generalize the concept of motion to include the part of the particle which is shared with other particles - and consequently has a form of "complete" oscillation. This leads to a fundamental revision of general relativity versus special relativity in light of the resulting overlap of the realms. On the basis of this generalized definition both of these realms are, in fact, the same.

Finally I will elaborate on Prof. Sadegh Angha's model of the unified presentation of all forces of nature.[1] I introduce his theory of inspiration, and show that indeed the inspiration scheme is the unified scheme to represent all fields of physics, including the mechanical ones.

25 - THE BREATHING OF PROTON AND NUCLEUS.

One of the characteristics of inspiration is the expansion of the system in which it occurs. Examples of this are the expansion of the lungs and hemoglobin molecules during the intake of O_2. On the other hand, the fusion of nuclei results in an increase or decrease in the nuclear penetration radius as follows.

Figure 1 shows the experimental plot of mass per nucleon versus the atomic number (i.e., the number of protons plus that of the neutrons). For nuclei less massive than Fe, the mass per nucleon decreases as the atomic number increases. Conversely, for those nuclei more massive than Fe, the mass per nucleon increases as the atomic number increases. Thus, the fusion of the first group of nuclei results in a release of some energy whereas the fusion of the second group of nuclei requires energy. Therefore the fusion of two "free" protons results in a nucleus (He^{++}) whose protons are less massive composed of "full" E&M waves rather than half waves. Professor Angha shows that this distribution of energy is in effect the particle neutron. Figure 2 shows a schematic of θ variation of $\vec{E_r}$ for a proton for a constant "r" where "r" is much larger than the penetration radius of the proton and yet microscopically small and $\phi = \pi/2$ and $3\,\pi/2$. As the figure shows, the oscillation of the electric field is "positive".[1]

Figure 3 shows a schematic of θ variation of $\vec{E_r}$ of a neutron for a constant "r" much larger than the penetration radius of the neutron yet microscopically small and $\phi = \pi/2$ and $3\pi/2$. As this figure shows, the variation of the electric field is oscillatory.[1]

When a proton combines with a neutron, a deuteron is formed. In order to facilitate understanding of the mechanism of deuteron formation, I suggest the following model: Figure 3 shows the full wave oscillations of the neutron, containing both the negative and the positive oscillations of the field. On the other hand, figure 2 shows the half wave oscillations of the proton, containing only the positive oscillations of the field. The full wave oscillations of the neutron seek those oscillations, which can fill the "valleys" and "hills" of its field oscillations. This explains the attraction of a neutron and anti-neutron. When a neutron encounters a proton of a right spin, the negative oscillations of the neutron match the positive oscillations of the proton. In this case the positive oscillations of the neutron remain bare and act like a proton. However, this matching and subsequent production of full oscillations leads to the quantized radiation from the "newly born" system, i.e., the deuteron.

In Professor Sadegh Angha's (PSA) theory, the formation of light resulting from the matching of systems is always accompanied by quantized radiation from the newly born system. Every time a system is formed, we must solve the PSA's wave equation

$$\nabla^2\ \xi(\vec{r}) = -(W_0\,W/\hbar^2\,c^2)\,\xi(\vec{r}) \qquad (1)$$

and find the energy levels of the radiation or the energies that the system radiates.[1] The case of the proton-neutron system is similar to that of the formation of the H atom. In the case of the H atom, the negative oscillations (the electron) partially match the positive oscillations (the proton). Then, classically, half of the full oscillations formed could leave the system. After solving his wave equation, Prof. Sadegh Angha shows that the energy levels indeed agree with the experimental ones as well as with the results of traditional quantum mechanics.[1]

In solving the wave equation for radiation of the proton-neutron system, we realize that the radiation energy present in this system is the neutron itself. Thus the total tradable energy W_0 is equal to $m_0c^2/2$ where m_0c^2 is the rest energy of the neutron. The radiation energy is $W = e^2/2r$ where "r" is measured from the center of the D. Hence PSA's wave equation for the formation of the deuteron is

$$\nabla^2 \, \xi(\vec{r}) = - \, (m_0 \, e^2 \, / \, 4r \, \hbar^2) \, \xi(\vec{r}). \qquad (2)$$

This resembles the wave equation for the H atom.[1] The quantized or allowed radii where the radiation can separate from the system (the nodes) are at:

$$r_n = \frac{\pi^2 \, n^2 \, e^2}{m_0 \, c^2} = 2 \, \pi^2 \, n^2 \, r_0, \qquad (3)$$

where r_0 is the penetration radius of the proton. Therefore the quantized allowed energies for the separable radiation from the deuteron are

$$W_n = \frac{e^2}{2r_n} = \frac{m_0 c^2}{2\pi^2 n^2} = \frac{W_0}{2\pi^2 n^2} \tag{4}$$

The rest mass of the H atom is 1.007825 u (1 u = 931.48 MeV) and that of the deuteron is 2.014102 u.[2] The mass of the neutron is 1.008665 u . The equation to find the nuclear binding energy is [2]

$$M(A, Z) = Z M_H + (A - Z) M_n - E_B/c^2, \tag{5}$$

where M(A, Z) is the mass of the nucleus, M_H is the rest mass of the H atom, M_n is the mass of a neutron, and E_B is the binding energy of the nucleus. Placing the masses into Eq. (5), the binding energy of the D is found to be 2.22 MeV. Furthermore, Professor Sadegh Angha has shown that n=k + $l/2$+ 1with k = 0, 1, 2, ... and l being the angular momentum.[1]

For n = 4.5, the radiated energy of the deuteron is [from Eq. (4)] 2.35 MeV which is 5.5% larger but in good agreement with the experimental value of 2.22 MeV. Later I will discuss the detailed formation of nuclei in the context of the PSA theory.

The primary role of the proton in the deuteron nucleus is to maintain the integrity of the neutron since a "bare" neutron disintegrates in about 11 minutes.[2] The negative oscillations of the neutron match the proton, and the positive part of the field oscillation remains bare. This is of crucial importance, in addition to explaining why the D nuclei still repel each other. The positive part is the equivalent positive charge of the proton, which is responsible for the repelling force. As in traditional nuclear physics, we can calculate the energy needed to put the deuterons together using the Coulomb energy equation $W = e^2/r$; where we take $1.12 \times 10^{-13} \leq r \leq 5 \times 10^{-13}$ cm, i.e., about the radius of the proton itself. This energy is $0.2880 \leq W \leq 1.2857$ MeV. In traditional nuclear physics this is the energy needed to bring two deuterons to a distance such that "the nuclear Strong force dominates over the electrostatic repulsion" of the protons.[3] In the PSA's theory, on the other hand, there is no duality of the electrostatic and the nuclear strong forces.[1] Here, the neutron is the glue that connects the protons together, and the reason the deuterons need some additional energy to come together is the fact that each proton-neutron system has radiated (its binding) energy. Therefore in order to fuse two deuterons we must first replace the radiated energy (the lost binding energy of the proton and the neutron) in each deuteron. Only then can the deuterons be combined.

As in the case of the deuteron, we can solve the PSA wave equation for the nucleus produced by the union of two deuterons. The three routes of fusion are:

$$_1^2D + \, _1^2D \rightarrow \, _2^3He + \, _0^1n \, + 3.27 \, MeV \qquad (6\text{-}9)$$

$$_1^2D + \, _1^2D \rightarrow \, _1^3T + \, _1^1H \, + 4.03 \, MeV \qquad (6\text{-}b)$$

$$_1^2D + \, _1^3T \rightarrow \, _2^4He + \, _0^1n + 17.6 \, MeV. \qquad (6\text{-}c)$$

To find the allowed radiated energies of ^{3}He in case (6-a), we have to write the PSA wave equation for the radiation energy of ^{3}He. The radiation energy present in ^{3}He is its only neutron. Hence the total tradable radiation energy of this nucleus is again the Total Radiation Energy available, i.e., (TRE)$= m_0c^2/2$ with m_0 being the rest mass of the neutron. However in order to keep the two protons together, this single neutron has to have a spatial distribution of energy $W = e^2/r$ rather than half of that as in the case of D. In this case we can show[1]

$$r_n = \frac{\pi^2 \, n^2 \, e^2}{2 \, m_0 \, c^2} = \pi^2 \, n^2 \, r_0, \qquad (7)$$

and

$$W_n = \frac{e^2}{r_n} = \frac{2 \, m_0 \, c^2}{\pi^2 \, n^2} = \frac{2 \, W_0}{\pi^2 \, n^2}. \qquad (8)$$

Using Eq. (5), we can calculate the binding energy of ^{3}He. We have $E_B/c^2 = Z \, M_H + (A - Z)M_n - M(A, Z)$. There are two protons and one neutron present in ^{3}He and its rest

mass is 3.016030 u. Therefore the binding energy of ^{3}He is

2 (1.007825) + 1.008665 - 3.016030 = 0.008285 u = 7.72

MeV. On the other hand regarding the fact that, in equation

(8), W_0 = 939.55 MeV, if we take n = 5, we have W_5 = 7.62

MeV, which varies only 1.3% from the experimental value of

7.72 MeV.

For the reaction (6-b), we solve the PSA's wave

equation for the radiation energy of ^{3}T. Here the radiation

energy present in ^{3}T is composed of two neutrons. Hence, the

total tradable radiation energy of this nucleus is $W_0 = m_0 c^2$

with m_0 being the rest mass of the neutron. Since we have

only one proton in ^{3}T, the spatial distribution of the radiation

energy should be $W = e^2/2r$, i.e., that of the one proton

present. In this case we can show

$$r_n = \frac{\pi^2 n^2 e^2}{2 m_0 c^2} = \pi^2 n^2 r_0, \qquad (9)$$

and

$$W_n = \frac{e^2}{2r_n} = \frac{m_0 c^2}{\pi^2 n^2} = \frac{W_0}{\pi^2 n^2} \qquad (10)$$

Again using Eq. (5), we can calculate the binding energy of ^{3}T. From Eq. (5) we have $E_B/c^2 = Z\,M_H + (A - Z)\,M_n - M\,(A, Z)$. The nucleus ^{3}T, has two neutrons and one proton, and its rest mass is 3.016050 u. Accordingly, the binding energy of ^{3}He is 1.007825 + 2(1.008665) - 3.016050 = 0.009105 u = 8.48 MeV. Regarding the fact that W_0 = 939.55 MeV, for n = 3.5, we have W_n = 7.77 MeV; which varies 8.4% from the experimental value of 8.48 MeV.

Finally, for the reaction of type (6-c), we solve the PSA's wave equation for the radiation energy of ^{4}He. The radiation energy present in ^{4}He is composed of two neutrons. Hence, the total tradable radiation energy of this nucleus is TRE = $m_0 c^2$. In this case, where we have two protons in ^{4}He, the spatial distribution of the radiation energy is $W = e^2/r$. We can show:

$$r_n = \frac{\pi^2 n^2 e^2}{4\,m_0\,c^2} = \frac{\pi^2 n^2 r_0}{2} \tag{11}$$

and

$$W_n = \frac{e^2}{r_n} = \frac{4\,m_0\,c^2}{\pi^2 n^2} = \frac{4\,W_0}{\pi^2 n^2} \tag{12}$$

Again, using Eq. (5), we can calculate the binding energy of ^{4}He. With the mass of ^{4}He being 4.002603 u; the binding energy of ^{4}He is 2(1.007825) + 2(1.008665) - 4.002603 = 0.030377 u = 28.3 MeV. Regarding the fact that $W_0 = 939.55$ MeV, for $n = 3.5^1$, we have $W_n = 31.1$ MeV; which varies 8.9% from the experimental value of 28.3 MeV.

In all of the above cases the angular part of the PSA's wave equation is similar to that of the H atom; thus, $n - 1 \geq l/2$ where l is the angular momentum of the system. Professor Sadegh Angha has discussed the reason for the acceptable half integer values of the angular momentum.[1]

Now that I have illustrated the general trend in finding the radiation (or binding) energies, it is necessary to elucidate the particle expansion and contraction. As discussed earlier, the matching of components to form a system is accompanied by some radiation. This is what physicists call "the binding energy" of the components. As a result of this radiation, each of the system components has a smaller rest energy than it does when it is free of the other. This decrease in the rest energy results in an increase in the penetration radius of the particles of each component. Consequently, the penetration radius of the whole system increases. Therefore, in general, a newly produced system has a *larger* volume than the combined volume of its components before they were united.

The penetration radius of a particle, e.g., a proton, at rest is $r_0 = e^2/2m_0c^2$ where m_0 is the rest mass of the particle. After sharing energy (and before the binding energy has left the system), we assume that each particle to momentarily contain $2w_B$ of radiation energy from a radius "$r_1 > r_0$" down to the particle's penetration radius r_0.[1] Thus we have:

$$\frac{e^2}{2\,r_0} - \frac{e^2}{2\,r_1} = 2\,W_B \tag{13}$$

Professor Sadegh Angha defines the wavelength of the particle at any "r" as:[1]

$$\lambda = \frac{h}{e}\left(\frac{2r}{m_0}\right)^{1/2} \tag{14}$$

After sharing energy and the subsequent loss of the binding energy, the particle wavelength at "r", is not the same as before.   After the loss of the binding energy the particle redistributes itself such that the matter part has a penetration radius ρ_0 bellow which the radiation's full wave part extends.

The wavelength of the new particle at its new penetration radius ρ_0 must be equal to the wavelength of the old (i.e., before the radiation of the binding energy) particle at $r_1 > r_0$.

This guarantees the integrity of the new particle at the point where the matter part (half wave structure in case of charged particles) converts to the full-wave structure of the radiation part. We then have:

$$\frac{h}{e} \left(\frac{2r_1}{m_0} \right)^{1/2} = \frac{h}{e} \left(\frac{2\rho_0}{\mu_0} \right)^{1/2} \qquad (15)$$

or $r_1 = \dfrac{m_0 \, \rho_0}{\mu_0}$ which results in

$$r_1 = \frac{\rho_0^{\,2}}{r_0} \qquad (16)$$

than those free protons. The difference in mass is released as energy, according to $E = (\delta m)c^2$. In chapter one I mentioned that the average energy released after the fusion of two D nuclei (each with one proton and one neutron) is 8.3 MeV (1MeV = 1 million electron volt where 1 eV = 1.6 X10^{-19} J). I therefore assume that each proton loses about 2.1 MeV of energy. In essence, the m_0c^2 of a fused proton is 2.1 MeV less than that of a single free proton.

In his book <u>Theory of Particle Structure and Its Applications</u> [1] Professor Sadegh Angha talks about putting protons together to build larger nuclei. According to this theory, (in order to put two protons together within a distance of r_0, we need to invest energy of e^2/r_0) if the two protons penetrate each other all the way down to each other's penetration radius, then we need to invest a net energy of $2m_0c^2$; where m_0 is the rest mass of the proton. This invested energy should have the form of full "complete" E&M oscillations and have a spatial distribution identical to that of the two protons. The structure of half of this invested energy is then the same as that of the proton except that it is

Substituting this value in Eq. (13), we have $(e^2/2r_0)$ - $(e^2$ $r_0/2\rho_0^2)$ = 2 w_B or $(e^2/2r_0)\left[1 - (r_0^2/\rho_0^2)\right]$ = 2 w_B . Considering that $e^2/2r_0$ = W_0 after some algebraic manipulations we will have

$$\rho_0 = \frac{r_0}{\left[\, 1 - (\, 2\, w_B \,/\, W_0\,)\, \right]^{1/2}} \qquad (17)$$

This is the penetration radius of a particle's matter part, which has shared part of itself with other particles and has participated in the radiation of part of 2 w_B and presently shares the rest of 2 w_B with other particles. Obviously, if the particle lost all of its shared radiation energy, there would be no radiation part present in it and its penetration radius would be $r_0 = e^2/2(W_0 - \delta W)$; where δW is the lost energy. The latter equation is simply the definition of the penetration radius of a particle. However, we need to find the penetration radius of the new particle from Eq. (17) because this particle is a product of the old particle, having matched other particles and lost some shared energy but yet holding some radiation energy.

From Eq. (17), $\rho_0 = e^2/2\,\mu_0\,c^2$, and $r_0 = e^2/2m_0c^2$ we can show

$$\mu_0 = m_0 \left[1 - (2\,w_B/W_0)\right]^{1/2}; \qquad (18)$$

which gives the mass of the matched particle in terms of its initial bond-free mass. Equation (18) expresses that *whenever the particle binds to other particles forming more complex systems or fields, it loses some of its rest mass through sharing with the other particles as well as radiating the binding energy.* This is a complement to Einstein's equation of mass increase for speeding particles, which are injected with kinetic energy. I will return to this important equation later in this chapter.

Consequently, when combining with other particles, a particle forms some radiation energy. Part of the shared radiation energy leaves the collective system of the particles while the rest is shared by the particles themselves. Later I will illustrate that in the classical case of $2\,w_B \ll W_0$, the radiated energy is indeed equal to w_B and the remaining radiation is also w_B. This radiated energy is the binding energy of the system. Consequently, this matching increases the penetration radius of the "matter part" of the particle (which is the penetration radius of the half wave part). I call this increase the *inspiration* of the particle.

As previously demonstrated, in its fusion with the neutron, the proton loses its binding energy and then shares the radiation energy with the neutron. The binding energy of the deuteron is 2.225 MeV. Thus, according to Eq. (17), the penetration radius of the proton in the deuteron is

$$\rho_0 = r_0 \Big/ \Big[1 - (2.225/938.3) \Big]^{1/2} \quad \text{or} \quad \rho_0 = 1.0012 \ r_0.$$

Therefore, the new radius of the proton is 0.12% larger than its initial penetration radius. The volume of the penetration sphere changes by 0.36%. *Therefore, after the proton matches the neutron, thereby forming the deuteron, it expands; i.e., it inspires.*

In Theory of Particle Structure and Its Applications[1] Prof. Sadegh Angha talks about the injection of kinetic energy (KE) into a particle, being the same as the matching of a particle with an opposite field.[1]   There he shows that the assumption of matching the field with a particle and forming the "radiation" energy $M v^2$ that has the form of complete E&M oscillations results in the following equation

$$R_0 = r_0 \left[1 - (v^2/c^2) \right]^{1/2},$$

(19)

where R_0 and r_0 are the penetration radii of the particle after (including the radiation) and before the matching, v is the speed of the particle, and $c = 3 \times 10^8$ m/s (the speed of light in "vacuum").   He found the mass of the moving particle in terms of its rest mass to be

$$M = \frac{m_0}{\left[1 - (v^2/c^2) \right]^{1/2}}$$

(20)

This is in agreement with the relativistic results. Therefore, the "extra" kinetic energy given by the field matches the particle to form $M v^2$ of light trapped in the particle. This extra energy gives the particle a "new" and smaller penetration radius and a bigger mass. These results are driven without appealing to the principles of relativity, rather simply on the basis of the theory of particle structure. Therefore, by matching the opposite field, the particle gains kinetic energy. This results in a reduction of the penetration radius of the particle. I call this the *expiration* of the particle. I will discuss this in more detail later.

Referring back to Fig 1 for nuclei less massive than Fe, the heavier nuclei have a smaller mass per nucleon than the lighter ones. This means the radius of the nucleon in the heavier nuclei is larger than that in lighter ones. Thus, for nuclei lighter than Fe, it is as if the fusion of the nuclei is an inspiration of their nucleons, i.e., an inspiration of the nucleus itself. On the other hand, for nuclei more massive than Fe, fusion results in an increase in the mass per nucleon, meaning the radius of the nucleon decreases as a result of fusion. This means that for these nuclei, fusion is an expiration of the nucleons; i.e., an expiration of the nucleus itself. Conversely, fission of such nuclei (which results in a smaller mass per nucleon) results in an increase in the radii of the component nucleons or their inspiration.

26 - THE BREATHING OF AN ATOM

The simplest atom in nature is the <u>H</u>ydrogen atom. It is composed of an electron which has matched a proton down to a radius - measured from the center of the proton – of approximately 0.5 Angstrom (1 Angstrom = 1 X 10^{-8} cm).[1] The reason for the matching of these particles both according to classical E&M theory and that of PSA is the attraction of the two particles. However, the following is how Prof. Sadegh Angha explains this attractive energy:[1] The electron is conformed of negative field oscillations half waves, and the proton is conformed of positive field oscillations half waves. The natural tendency of particles is to interact in a way that leads to the production of light. Being approximately 2000 times stronger, the positive field of the proton attracts the negative field (i.e., the electron) and matches it where the wavelength of the two fields match.[1] Professor Angha shows that the partial matching of the two fields continues down to a radius - measured from the center of the proton – of approximately 0.5 Angstrom, i.e., the Bohr radius. In this process, some light is produced as a result of the partial matching of the two fields. Since the matched part shared by the two fields also has a distribution of energy twice as large as the unmatched parts, half of the matched part (in the form of a complete oscillatory field, i.e., light) is radiated. This radiated energy is taken equally from the electron's and the proton's field, i.e., rest energy. The magnitude of the radiated energy in both PSA's theory and traditional quantum mechanics is approximately 13.6 eV. Referring to Eq. (17), - and noting that both the electron and the proton lose part of their rest energy as radiation - we realize that in the process of conforming the H atom both the electron and the proton expand. *In essence, both the electron and proton inspire in the process of the birth of the H atom.* From Eq. (17), we can show.

$$\frac{\delta r}{r_0} = \left\{ 1 \Big/ \left[\, 1 - (\, 2 \, w_B \big/ W_0 \,) \, \right]^{1/2} \right\} - 1$$

The fractional change of the electron's radius is then

$$\left(\frac{\delta r}{r_0} \right)_e = \left\{ 1 \Big/ \left[\, 1 - (\, 27.2 \big/ 5.12 \mathrm{X} 10^5) \, \right]^{1/2} \right\} - 1$$

$= 2.66 \times 10^{-5}$ or $(\delta r/r_0)_e = 2.66 \times 10^{-3}$ %. For the proton

this ratio is about 2000 times smaller.

Thus, the binding of the electron to the nucleus is the inspiration of the participating components. Conversely, the destruction of the atom, i.e., the ionization of the electrons, occurs while the system of the electron-nucleus gains the radiated energy. This increases the rest energy of both the electron and the nucleus; meaning their radii decrease, i.e., they expire.

27 - THE BREATHING OF MOLECULES AND MORE COMPLEX SYSTEMS

Atoms attract each other, bind, and form molecules. In PSA's theory of particle structure this attractive energy is modeled as follows. The electrons are bound to the atom because they partially match the nucleus and the resulting electron-nucleus system radiates a quantized part of the shared energy. Once this energy is donated to the atom, the electrons and nucleus regain their normal field energy. They then "untangle" and become free of each other. Thus, in its bound state, the electrons-nucleus system of the atom is missing some of its radiation energy. Once this atom is in the proximity of another atom of the same type, the two incomplete shared electron-nucleus fields "see" each other and attempt to complement each other. This is due to the trapped radiation energy left in their system. Since they have exactly the same distribution of trapped radiation, they are able to perfectly match each other. The distribution of this energy is different than that of a free atom in that the energy must "sew" the electrons and the protons of the two atoms to each other just as when the neutron connects the protons to each other. By matching these fields and solving the PSA wave equation for them, we can arrive at the molecular binding energies.[4]

Let us start with the calculation of the binding energies of the H_2 molecule. The case of the H_2^+ is very similar to case (6-a); where we calculated the binding energy of the ^3He nucleus. Similar to that case we have some radiation energy (in this case $W_0 = 13.6$ eV) which, like the neutron in the case of ^3He, binds two protons together. In the present case the total tradable radiation energy is $W_0/2 = 13.6/2 = 6.8$ eV. There, I showed that we could find the spectrum of the binding energy from the Eq. (8) or $W_n = 2 W_0 / \pi^2 n^2$. For $n = 1$, we have $W_1 = 2.756$ eV. The experimental value for the binding energy of H_2^+ is 2.79 eV [5] which is only 1.2% larger than our value.

Moving on to the calculation of the binding energy of H_2, this is how we approach the problem: Holding two H atoms infinitely far from each other, we bring them close to each other. The first step is that one of the full waves (bound to one of the atoms) forms a bond between the two protons just as in the case of H_2^+. After this process, the energy that this full wave has available is 13.6 - 2.756 = 10.844 eV. Next this full wave energy and the same amount from the other full wave of the second atom match to bind the electrons as well as further bind the protons. Thus at this stage, the total tradable energy is 10.844 eV (= $2W_0/2$). Therefore, in this case there are two electrons to bind and also two protons to bind, then the spatial distribution of the radiation energy should be $4(e^2/2r)$. Appendix I will show that if the total tradable energy is W_t and the distribution of the binding radiation is $N (e^2/2r)$, then the tradable radiation energy of the system (which is the same as the dissociation energy of the system) is

$$W_n = \frac{N^2 W_t}{\pi^2 n^2} \quad , \qquad (21)$$

Here the tradable energies are

$$W_n = \frac{4^2 (10.844 \text{ eV})}{\pi^2 n^2} = 17.580 \text{ eV}/n , \qquad (22)$$

For n = 1, we have W_1 = 17.580 eV which is larger than the total tradable energy, i.e. 10.844 eV, and thus, not acceptable. For n = 2, we have W_2 = 4.395 eV. Since the first full wave has released 2.756 eV, then 2.756 eV from this (4.395 eV) will be given to the first full wave. In this case both of the bound waves of the atoms have shared equally in the molecular binding energy. Thus the total energy released is 4.395 eV. The experimental value for the binding of the H atoms in an H_2 molecule is 4.48 eV,[2] which is only 1.9% larger than this value.

In traditional quantum mechanics, the problem of the binding energy of the H_2^+ and H_2 molecules are treated with cumbersome approximation methods since the exact problem is very difficult to solve. Molecular physicists and chemists can perhaps appreciate the simplicity of the present approach more so than others who are less familiar with the labor involved in these kinds of calculations - especially with theoretical values of the binding energies approximating so closely the experimental values.

Here I would like to postpone the problem of calculation of the molecular binding energies in order to return to the issue of molecular breathing. In the process of forming molecules, atoms lose some of their trapped energies. This means that according to Eq. (17), the penetration radius of the atom is increased and its rest mass decreases, resulting in a rest mass of the molecule that is less than the combined totals of its components. Again, an increase in the penetration radius of the atom is the indication of its inspiration. In other words, rather than using the term binding energy, one could speak of the increase in the penetration radius of the atom or its inspiration. I will come back to this suggestion in section 11 on Prof. Sadegh Angha's inspiration theory.

Similar molecules also attract one another precisely because they need to complement their trapped radiation energy. The incomplete trapped light of two molecules (which have lost binding energies) then match to complement each other. Subsequently, part of the shared-trapped radiation emerges from the system of the two molecules. Similarly, two systems of two molecules each attract one another to complement the other's missing trapped radiation. Each time two systems join to form a single system some of the shared-trapped radiation leaves the newly formed system. This is actually what physicists have called the binding energy of the systems. The fact that some of the energy of the components leaves the system means that the penetration radii of the components increase leading to their inspiration, which in turn results in the inspiration of the whole system.

This process continues every time two systems confront each other all the way to the macroscopic level. Obviously the occurrence of the bond between molecules depends on their kinetic energy. For gases there is no chance of bonding to occur because of their relatively high kinetic energy. After some of the kinetic energy is absorbed (including the latent heat of vaporization) the gas liquefies. In the liquid state molecules have the chance to form a temporary bond with each other. The viscosity of a liquid is an indication of, on the average, how closely molecules are bound. Once again, in the process of binding molecules release energy, ultimately causing the atoms to lose energy and thus their radii increase or they inspire. The inspiration (or expansion) of the individual atoms results in the inspiration of the whole system.

The conversion of a liquid to a solid is also accompanied by loss of kinetic energy including the latent heat of fusion. According to Eq. (19), this means that molecules go through an inspiration because their speed decreases. In solids the atoms and molecules are much more tightly bound together than in liquids. The binding among neighbors is so strong that the atoms or molecules of the solid do not get the chance to move around but only oscillate about their equilibrium point. The equilibrium point is the position where the net force on the atom (or molecule) is zero. In classical solid-state physics, the solids are classified according to the type of bond between the atoms (or molecules).[2] No matter what class of solid one deals with, the binding energy among the atoms is the released radiation due to the matching between the bound full waves of the atoms. The release of the binding energy - once the solid is formed - is again an indication of an increase in the atomic radii. *Here again, the inspiration of the ensemble of the atoms results in the birth of a new system - in this case a solid.*

When two solids are in contact, the atoms (or molecules) of their neighboring surfaces temporarily bind with each other. This is in fact the reason for friction. The binding of the atoms (or molecules) of the surfaces is the same as their inspiration. More unification of the systems results in a larger number of the inspiring atoms. *Thus, in terrestrial objects their binding results in the internal expansion of their atoms, i.e., their inspiration.*

28 - GRAVITATIONAL BREATHING

One of the many achievements of PSA's theory of particle structure is the demonstration of the unified nature of gravitational energy with electromagnetic energy. Let us briefly look at this model of gravitational energy.[1]

The story of the birth of gravitational energy starts with the formation of trapped radiation energy; e.g., the H atom. In the H atom the negative and positive fields, i.e., the electron and the proton, partially match and form complete E&M oscillations (light) within the matched region. Since the distribution of energy in this shared region is twice as much as the other parts of the particles half of the shared light is radiated to preserve the initial distribution of energy in the individual particles. PSA's results and the experimental electronic energy levels are in excellent agreement.

After part of the shared energy leaves the atom, the electron rearranges its energy distribution around the center of the proton or atom. The shared light also redistributes itself around the center of the proton. At this stage the gravitational energy of the H atom is born. *Naturally, the trapped part of the shared radiation wants to free itself from the atom; but only a small part of it is freed because this radiation is in fact a part of the atom;[1] i.e., part of the very structure of the electron and the proton.*

As seen in the previous section, by sharing itself among atoms, this remaining radiation of the electrons-nucleus system frees part of itself. *The gravitational part is that part of the shared radiation which is freed from the individual atom just because this radiation is caught in the atom while it is light.* This is a completely different case than that of two atoms sharing their radiation and subsequently radiating part of the total radiation.

Starting from the H atom, the total amount of the trapped radiation energy is smaller than that of the electron by a factor $2(m_e/\pi^2 M_p)$, which we define as 2β.[1] Here m_e is the rest mass of the electron and M_p is the rest mass of the proton. If this radiation were not caught by the electron and the proton, it would be free to travel in space. However, the electron and proton each place a constraint on this freedom. The penetration of the radiation is only to $2(r_0)_e$, where $(r_0)_e$

is the penetration radius of the electron. The distribution of this radiation is by a factor β, smaller than that of the electron or the proton; which means both the electron and the proton are holding onto this light with a relative strength of β^{-1}.

Therefore, the electron and the proton each allow only $(m_e/\pi^2 M_p) = \beta$ part of this light to leave the system. Thus, classically, at a point "r", only $\beta^3 e^2/2r$ ergs leaves the electron-proton system. Here $e^2/2r$ is the electron's or the proton's energy distribution in space and "r" is the radial distance from the center of the proton, which is now the center of the atom. Since this is a quantum mechanical radiation, Professor Sadegh Angha solves his wave equation for it and the net radiated part of the shared light of H atom turns out to be $(W_G)_{PSA} = -1.03 \ (\beta^8/\pi^4)e^2/2r$.[1] Here, the subscript G refers to the gravitational, and subscript "PSA" refers to the fact that this is the PSA E&M radiation. The Newtonian self-gravitational energy of the H atom is $(W_G)_N = -\ (G \ m_H^2/e^2)(e^2/2r)$ where G $(= 6.670 \ \times \ 10^{-11}$ $N.m^2/kg^2)$ is the universal gravitational constant and the subscript N refers to "Newtonian". Comparison of $(W_G)_{PSA}$

with $(W_G)_N$ results in 11% difference. *Thus, the ground state energy of the lost part of the trapped light of the H atom is its gravitational energy.* Here the beauty of the PSA's model lies within the fact that this radiation is of E&M type while at the same time it is the gravitational energy of the atom. *Thus the E&M and gravitational energies are the same.* The gravitational energy of N hydrogen atoms placed at a small distance with respect to one another is also found to be - $N^2 G \, m_H{}^2 / 2r$, i.e., the same as that from Newton's law. The negative sign of the gravitational energy means that it is radiated, or lost by the system.

Losing even this small part of its radiation energy, an atom redistributes itself to fill the space with its initial (i.e. before radiation) energy distribution. Having made a bond according to Eq. (17), the penetration radii of both the electron and the proton increase. In essence, *the radiation from the trapped light of the H atom or the gravitational energy causes an increase in the radius of the atom itself or the atom's inspiration.* I term this "Gravitational Inspiration." Once two similar atoms are bound, the gravitational energy at any point is four times larger, meaning the atoms have lost more energy and thus their radii have increased even more. In other words, they have inspired more. Putting N atoms together the energy loss by each atom is N^2 times that when the atom is alone. Thus the radius of the atom has increased N consecutive times (not by a factor N) during this gravitational interaction, meaning it has inspired N times. The reverse case is also true; when we separate an atom from the other ones, it regains this lost radiation, and therefore its penetration radius decreases. I call this "gravitational expiration."

The gravitational expansion of ordinary size objects is very small, due to the fact that the gravitational self-energy loss of the system is very small. For objects of astronomical size, even though the relative expansion is still very small, the magnitude of the inspiration itself is very large. This is because the gravitational radiation loss is itself very large. The self-gravitational energy of a sphere with a mass of M and radius R is

$$W_G = - \frac{3\,G\,M^2}{5\,R} \quad , \tag{23}$$

Using Eq. (17) to determine the change in the radius, we have

$$\delta R = R \left\{ -1 + 1 \Big/ \left[1 - (2\,|W_G|/W_0) \right]^{1/2} \right\} \qquad (24)$$

where we have replaced 2 w$_B$ with 2 $|W_G|$ since the binding energy is the same as the self-gravitational energy in this case. Substituting W_G by the right hand side of the Eq. (23) and W_0 by Mc^2, we have:

$$\delta R = R \left\{ -1 + 1 \Big/ \left[1 - (6G\,M/5R\,c^2) \right]^{1/2} \right\} \qquad (25)$$

For the earth we have R $=$ 6.37 X 10^6 m and M $=$ 5.976 X 10^{24} kg thus the term $6\,G\,M/5\,R\,c^2 = 8.34$ X 10^{-10}. Therefore, to a good approximation, for planets we can substitute $1/\left[1 - (6\,G\,M/5\,R\,c^2) \right]^{1/2}$ term by 1 + (3 G M$/5\,R\,c^2$). In this case we have

$$\delta R = \frac{3\,G\,M}{5\,c^2} \quad , \qquad (26)$$

Therefore to the first approximation, the term δR is independent of the radius of the planet or the star. The magnitude of δR for the earth is 2.66×10^{-3} m. Obviously compared to the radius of the earth ($R = 6.37 \times 10^6$ m) this is a very small change. The magnitude of the earth's volume expansion due to this change is $\delta V_e = 4\pi R^2 \delta R = 13.54 \times 10^{11}$ m³; therefore it is considerably larger. However, compared to the volume of the earth itself ($V = 4\pi R^3/3 = 1.08 \times 10^{21}$ m³), the δV is still very small.

For the sun we have $R = 0.695 \times 10^9$ m and $M = 1.991 \times 10^{30}$ kg.[6] In that case from Eq. (26), $\delta R_s = 8.86 \times 10^2$ m, which is very small, compared to the radius of the sun itself. The magnitude of the volume expansion is $\delta V_s = 5.38 \times 10^{21}$ m³. Although compared to the volume of the sun ($V = 1.41 \times 10^{27}$ m³) this is 2.62×10^5 times smaller, still this change is about 4.97 times the total volume of the earth.

Using the same method, we can calculate the gravitational inspiration for other planets and astronomical objects. One should note, however, that only when the components get together and form the object is there a gravitational inspiration. Similarly, only when the components separate is there gravitational expiration. The gravitational force among its components, however, preserves the integrity of an object. This is especially remarkable in the case of astronomical objects. In summary, gravitational attraction causes a one-time inspiration when components of objects get together. The magnitude of inspiration is intimately related to the strength of the gravitational field. In other words rather than speaking of the strength of the gravitational field, one could talk about the degree of the inspiration of the objects. I will discuss this in detail later in this chapter.

The formation of the galaxies, which took place through the accumulation of H atoms, was a gravitational inspiration. On the other hand, separation of the planets from the sun to form the solar system was a gravitational expiration of the sun as well as of the planets themselves. Throughout the universe these inspirations and expirations are indications of the birth of one system out of the death of another.

29 - THE BREATHING OF THE SUN

In our solar system the sun is the source of energy. The sun is at the center of the solar system and has a mass of $M = 1.991 \times 10^{30}$ kg - about 333500 times more massive than the earth. The radius of the sun is $R = 0.695 \times 10^{9}$ m- about 109 times the radius of the earth. Figure 4 shows a schematic of the sun and it's calculated temperature and density of the internal and external layers. The core of the sun is its hottest part, with an approximate temperature of 15.4 million degrees Kelvin ($K = C^{o} + 273$). The density of the center of the sun is about 158-g/cm^{3}. As we move from the center toward the surface of the sun, the temperature, density, and pressure decrease. The gravitational pressure at the center of the sun is $P = 2.7 \times 10^{14}$ pascals or about 2.665 billion atmospheres.[6]

Each second, approximately 4×10^{9} kg of mass is converted to energy in the sun. According to Einstein's equation $E = m c^{2}$, this is equivalent to 3.6×10^{26} Watts or Joules per second. The source of this energy is the nuclear fusion at the core of the sun. The radius of the core of the sun is about $R_{core} = 0.25R = 1.7375 \times 10^{8}$ m. No nuclear fusion takes place beyond the core because of the temperature being lower than that needed for fusion. The energy of the fusion is released in the form of the kinetic energy of the particles or the radiation, i.e., photons. On their way out of the core the photons collide with the particles present in the sun and produce either a pair of particle-antiparticle or secondary photons. Because of these collisions, the process of these photons leaving the core and coming to the surface of the sun takes millions of years. Consequently, the released energy from the photosphere of the sun is the energy that has been produced millions of years ago at the core of the sun.[6]

What changes happen when the enormous nuclear explosions take place in the sun? The energy of the explosions is released, accelerating the particles present in the core as well as producing a radiation pressure, thereby pushing out all of the layers exterior to the core. On the other hand, the gravitational attraction of the mass components of the core as well as that of the outer layers prevents any permanent expansion of the sun itself. Therefore, the resultant motion is an oscillatory motion of the layers around their equilibrium radii. In short, fusion produces an expansion of the sun; i.e., inspiration; and gravitational attraction brings the radius back to its original value; i.e., expiration. I refer to this as "the breathing of the sun." When breathing occurs in humans, the act of expansion of the lungs precedes the deuterons' fusion in mitochondria whereas in the breathing of the sun the fusion of deuterons precedes the sun's expansion. We can approximate the amount of the fusion expansion in the volume of the core after each second.

Let us assume that the energy of the fusion produced in the sun's core performs mechanical work on the particles of the core itself and in this fashion it expands the core's volume. From the definition of mechanical work on a gas we have $\delta W = P \, \delta V$; where δW is the work, P is the pressure, and δV is the change in the volume of the gas. Considering δW equal to the fusion power produced in the core, we have (for each second)

$$\delta W_f = P \, \delta V = 3.6 \times 10^{26} \text{ Joules.} \tag{27}$$

The normal approximate pressure change of the core is from $P = 2.7 \times 10^{14}$ pascals at the center of the sun to $P = 1 \times 10^{13}$

pascals at $R_{core} = 0.25\ R = 1.7375\ X\ 10^8 m$. Assuming an approximate linear P-R dependence, we take the average of these two pressures and take this to be the pressure all over the core. Thus, we take the pressure of the core $P_{core} = (2.7X10^{14} + 1X10^{13})/2 = 1.4\ X\ 10^{14}$ pascals. In this case we have $\delta W_f = 3.6\ X10^{26}$ Joules $= (1.4\ X\ 10^{14}$ Pascals) δV, or

$$\delta V_{core} = 2.57\ X\ 10^{12}\ m^3/s. \tag{28}$$

Therefore, due to nuclear fusion, the volume of the core momentarily expands. Although the value of this volume expansion is huge, it is a very small expansion relative to the volume of the core itself. Additionally, the δR_{core} that this volume expansion produces is very small. To see this, we note that $\delta V = 4\ \pi\ (R_{core})^2\ \delta R_{core}$. Using this equation, we find $\delta R_{core} = 8.26\ X\ 10^{-6}\ m$. Nonetheless, there indeed is a volume expansion in the core due to the nuclear fusion. Note that this is the amount of the volume expansion produced as a result of one second of fusion in the core. The age of the sun is estimated as 4.5 billion years. If the gravitational attraction did not prevent the fussional expansion, then the total expansion of the core of the sun would be

$$\delta V_{total} = \delta V_{core}\,\delta t = (2.57 \text{ X } 10^{12}\text{ m}^3/\text{s})(1.4191 \text{ X}10^{17}\text{ s})$$
$$= 3.65 \text{ X } 10^{29}\text{ m}^3. \tag{29}$$

Assuming the same total volume expansion for the sun itself and considering the fact that the volume of the sun is $V_s = 4\,\pi\,R_s^{\,3}/3 = 3.52 \text{ X}10^{26}\text{ m}^3$, we have $\delta V_{total}/V_s = 1.04\text{X}10^3$. This means that due to the fusion explosions at its core, the sun would expand to a volume about 1000 times its original volume during its life of 4.5 billion years.

Why then is there no permanent expansion of the sun? As mentioned before, the gravitational attraction among the mass components of the core prevents long term expansion. In essence, after a little expansion this gravitational attraction brings the core back to its original radius. Let us calculate the gravitational energy needed to allow the core to increase its radius by $\delta R_{core} = 8.26\text{X}10^{-6}$ m, which is the change due to fusion reactions. The core self-gravitational energy is $W_G = -\,3\,G\,(M_{core})^2\big/5\,R_{core}$. This is the energy needed to totally disintegrate the core's mass components; i.e., bring them to distances infinitely far from each other. The change in gravitational self-energy of a sphere due to a change in mass and radius is

$$\delta W_G = -\,(3\,G/5)\left\{\left[2M(\Delta M)\big/R\right]-\left[M^2\delta R\big/R^2\right]\right\}, \quad (30)$$

The mass of the core is almost half of the total mass of the sun itself $M_{core} = 9.95\,X10^{29}$ kg. Let's consider the fact that G $= 6.67\,X\,10^{-11}$ N m^2/kg^2, $\delta M_{core} = 4\,X10^9$ kg, and $R_{core} = 1.7375\,X\,10^8$ m, and $\delta R_{core} = 8.26\,X\,10^{-6}$ m, we can see that the first term in the bracket is about 10^6 times smaller than the second term and thus it can be ruled out. The result is

$$\delta W_G = 5.14\,X\,10^{27} \text{ Joules.} \quad (31)$$

Equation (31) shows that in order to expand the radius of the core of the sun by $\delta R_{core} = 8.26 \times 10^{-6}$ m, we have to provide it with $\delta W_G = 5.14 \times 10^{27}$ Joules of energy. Comparing this energy with that produced by the fusion reaction in one second, i.e., $W_f = 3.6 \times 10^{26}$ Joules, we realize that the energy produced through fusion is not enough to expand the core by $\delta V_{core} = 2.57 \times 10^{12}$ m^3/s; but perhaps by only 7% of that; i.e., 1.799×10^{11} m^3. After this expansion, the core contracts to its original volume and oscillates around its equilibrium radius.

The source of the sun's radiation is the fusion at its core. Fusion is the source of the energy needed for life. In this case it is the provider of life for a star; the one star that is the very source of life on earth and human beings on its surface. It is ultimately the breathing of the sun that makes human breathing and life possible. In other words, *the breathing of the sun eventually results in the breathing of the human beings on the earth's surface. It is the source of life on this planet.*

30 - The Breathing of the Earth and Other Planets.

The planet earth - the third planet from the sun - is one of the nine planets revolving around the sun and receiving radiation from it. The mean earth-sun distance is 1.4957×10^{11} m which is called one astronomical unit (1 AU). As previously mentioned, the mass and the radius of the earth are $M_e = 5.976 \times 10^{24}$ kg and $R_e = 6.37 \times 10^6$ m. The age of the earth is estimated to be 4.6 billion years. Astronomers now believe that the suns as well as the planets of the solar system were all formed from the condensation of the same original cloud of gas and dust. The gas started gravitating towards its center while materials with different melting points solidified at different distances from the sun. This model is called the *evolutionary* model, and is perhaps the most accepted theory of the origin of the solar system. The popularity of the evolutionary model is due to the fact that it can explain more of the observational facts than the other suggested models. Two other models for the origin and the evolution of the solar system are the Catastrophe and the

Capture models. The Catastrophe model claims that due to the collision of meteorites with the sun, the materials forming the planets were separated from the sun itself. The Capture model claims that the sun and the planets were formed in different places in the galaxy and later the sun captured the planets.[6]

Whatever the process of formation of the planets, the fact is that they have been formed out of gravitational attraction of the dust particles of the galaxy. Therefore, during this process, they have inspired. The gravitational attraction among the dust particles brought them closer to each other. This proximity in turn resulted in an increase in the self-gravitational field of the central core. We have seen that an increase in the binding energy of the particles results in a decrease in the rest energy of each component particle. Equation (17) shows the relation between the binding energy and the penetration radius of the particle, i.e., $\rho_0 = {}^r0 / \left[1 - (2 w_B / W_0) \right]^{1/2}$. An increase in w_B results in an increase in ρ_0. Consequently, in their process of formation, the planets as well as the sun itself have gone through inspirations.

Figure 5 shows the schematic of the earth's layers.[7]
We can only directly sample the crust of the earth, which is
estimated to vary in thickness from between 16 to 40 km.
Below the crust there is the mantle. The thickness of the
mantle has been estimated to be 2,900 km. Although the
material of the mantle is in a molten state, it is nevertheless in
a plastic shape because of its high pressure.[7] At a depth of
2,900 km below the surface, the realm of the liquid core of the
earth starts. At the interface between the mantel and the core
of the earth the average density changes - suddenly - from 5.5
g/cm^3 to 9.5 g/cm^3. Therefore, the "outer" core has to be
formed of denser material. The main element in this part is
believed to be iron in its molten state. The minimum
temperature of this part ($2,000^oC$) has been estimated to be
higher than the melting point of iron (about $1,550^oC$) and
seismic data confirm that this part is, in fact, in liquid state.
Finally, there is some evidence that there may be a solid inner
core of radius 1,220 km.[7]

One of the most frequent and large-scale changes on
the surface of the earth is the tidal effect of the moon and the
sun. The tidal effects are due to the gravitational attraction of

the moon and the sun on the surface of the earth. The tidal forces not only pull and push the earth's waters; they also have the same kind of effect on the earth's solid surface as well. However, the difference between the tides in the rocks and those in the water is that the response of the water is more pronounced than that of the solid rocks. The ocean tides are in fact the actual tide of the water minus that of the rocks themselves.[7]

Albert Michelson (1852-1931) is the first scientist who determined the ratio between the tides in the rocks and those in the water. He designed and built a micro-ocean for which one can easily calculate the total tidal rise of the water. His experimental measurement of the rise of the surface of the water in the micro ocean, however, compensated for only 69% of the calculated value. The remaining 31% difference must be due to the tidal movement of the solid surface of the earth itself. [7]

The oceanic tidal rise in the surface of the water amounts to 75 cm. But this only accounts for 69%, because the tidal forces affect the surface of the earth. Thus, the actual rise should be 109 cm. The 34-cm difference again must be due to the tidal rise of the solid surface of the earth itself. As George Gamoove expresses, *"Though strange as it seems, the ground under our feet is periodically moving up and down with all the cities, hills, and mountains on its surface. It is pulled (or pushed) up every time the moon is high in the sky (or is exactly under it on the other side of the earth) and sinks down again as soon as the moon approaches the horizon."*[7]

The tidal rise happens twice in 24 hours; once when the moon is directly above our head and then again when the moon is exactly on the opposite side of the earth. The reason for the occurrence of the tidal rise when the moon is on the opposite side of the earth is that the gravitational pull of the moon on the nearest side, the middle, and the far side of the earth is different. This force is strongest on the nearest side and weakest on the farthest side. Thus, the moon pulls the nearest side and the center of the earth with greater force than it pulls the far side of the earth. Consequently, the shift towards the moon of the far side is less than that of the center of the earth (fig, 6).

About 3/4 of the surface of the earth is covered with water. Considering this and the above measurements of the tidal rises, the average tidal rise of the surface of the earth is about 65 cm. Thus $\delta R = 0.65$ m which results in $\delta V = 4\pi R^2 .\delta R = 3.3 \times 10^{14}$ m^3. The total volume of the earth is 1.08×10^{21} m^3; thus the relative change in the volume of the earth is 3.05×10^{-7}. The term $\delta V = 3.3 \times 10^{14}$ m^3 expresses the tidal inspiration of the earth.

Using Eq. (30), for the present change in the radius, we have $\delta W_G = (3G/5)\left[M^2(\delta R)/R^2\right]$ where we have taken off the term which includes δM because there is no change in the mass of the earth in this case. Placing the 0.65m change of the radius, we have $\delta W_G = 2.28 \times 10^{25}$ J (the ratio $\delta W_G / W_G = \delta R/R = 1.02 \times 10^{-7}$). Since this is a small ratio, we can use Eq. (26) to find the additional self gravitational δR. Equation (26) is $\delta R = 3\,G\,M/5c^2$. In this case, it is $\delta R = 2.66 \times 10^{-3}$ m. This is a very small change in the radius of the earth; however, it results in a large change in the volume equal to $\delta V = 4\pi R^2 .\delta R = 13.54 \times 10^{11}$ m^3. Thus, the action of the tides is responsible for the additional gravitational breathing of the earth. This means the penetration radius of every atom of the earth increases, resulting in increasing the atomic volume. The term $\delta V =$ 13.54X10^{11} m^3 expresses the net change in the volume of the earth due to the atomic volume change produced by gravitational increase in the atomic penetration radii.

Tidal effects due to the gravitational attraction of the sun also occur. Nevertheless, these effects are much smaller than the lunar effects because of the much larger earth-sun distance. But during the full and new moon periods, when the sun, the moon, and the earth are on the same straight line, the solar and the lunar tides reinforce one another's pull on the earth's surface.[7]

There are other deformations which have occurred during the 4.6 billion years of the earth's existence. Every deformation has been accompanied by changes in the volume or redistribution of mass on the surface of the earth. We can then say that every deformation has been an inspiration or expiration of the earth itself. A few of these changes include the following. The earth's heat loss during the past 4.6 billion years has been estimated to be about 10^{30} calories (1 calorie = 4.18 Joule). This heat loss has been estimated to produce shrinkage of about 300 km in the circumference of the earth itself.   About $2X10^{16}$ m^3 has been washed away from the continents and carried to the oceans. This is an indication of a thickness of about 2-km of land having been washed away from the continents and carried to the oceans. Rainwater also washes away about 0.22 mm of the continents in to the oceans every year.[7]

31 - COMPARISON WITH GENERAL RELATIVISTIC RESULTS, BLACK HOLES.

What is the velocity of light in a field? How do the frequency and wavelength of a light emitted from the inside of the field compare with those outside of the field? How do the results of the present PSA approach to the gravitational fields compare with those of general relativity?

For Electro-Magnetic (E&M) fields the PSA theory has presented the effect of the field on the speed, frequency, and wavelength of an incoming light.[1] For outgoing lights the effect is reversed. The following is my approach to finding the data for gravitational field: Equations (17) and (18), i.e.,

$$\rho_0 = r_0 / \left[1 - (2\, w_B / W_0) \right]^{1/2} \text{ and}$$

$$\mu_0 = m_0 \left[1 - (2\, w_B / W_0) \right]^{1/2} \text{ respectively, show the}$$

radius and mass of a stationary particle having participated in the construction of a field. From Eq. (17) we deduce that the "r" of the old particle transfer to "ρ" of the new particle where

$$\rho = r / \left[1 - (2\, w_B / W_0) \right]^{1/2}.$$

Conversely, I mentioned in the PSA theory the wavelength of a particle at any "r" is defined as $\lambda_0 = (h/e)(2r/m_0)^{1/2}$. The light with wavelength λ_0 which would be emitted from "r" in the old particle is now emitted from "ρ" in the new particle. Thus the same light is radiated with $\lambda = (h/e)(2\rho/\mu_0)^{1/2}$. Substituting for p and μ_0 from above:

$$\lambda = (h/e)\left\{(2r/m_0)\left[1-(2w_B/W_0)\right]\right\}^{1/2} \text{ or}$$

$$\lambda = \lambda_0 / \left[1-(2w_B/W_0)\right]^{1/2}. \tag{32}$$

Note that λ_0 is the wavelength in the absence of the field, i.e., for the incoming light the wavelength at distances infinitely far from the particle. For nonrelativistic cases, i.e., $2w_B \ll W_0$, we can expand the term $\left[1-(2w_B/W_0)\right]^{-1/2}$. Doing this and keeping only the first order term in $2w_B/W_0$, we have $\lambda = \lambda_0\left[1+(w_B/W_0)\right]$ or $\delta\lambda/\lambda_0 = w_B/W_0$.

For light in a gravitational field the shared energy before the radiation of energy is $2w_B = 2GMW_0/rc^2$. Thus

$$(\delta \lambda / \lambda_0) = G \, M / r \, c^2 \qquad\qquad (33)$$

Which is exactly the same as the general relativistic results of gravitational red shift.[8] On the other hand in the limiting case of the denominator of the Eq. (32) going to zero; i.e., $2 \, w_B \approx W_0$, the new wavelength, λ will go to infinity which means no light will be able to escape from the field or the field is constituted by a black hole. Also from

$2 \, w_B = 2 \, G \, M \, W_0 / r \, c^2$, the equation $2 \, w_B \approx W_0$ will result

in $r = 2G \, M / c^2$. $\qquad\qquad (34)$

This is the Schwarzchild radius surrounding a black hole of mass M. It is the radius of the sphere around a black hole from which light cannot escape.[8]

Notice that contrary to the case of general relativity, it is not necessary to appeal to different domains of masses, lighter objects (e.g., normal stars and white dwarfs), on the one hand, and heavier objects (e.g. neutron stars and black holes) on the other.[6,8] Equation (32) is of major significance because it applies to all fields and it covers the entire spectrum of masses for gravitational fields. It should be noted furthermore, that a black hole is a possibility in the case of "every" field and is not just limited to gravitational fields. In essence, when all of the "rest" energy of the particles of the field has been shared and converted either to trapped or to radiated energy that system no longer radiates energy; rather, it attracts all radiation in order to replace that energy which was lost.

In order to find the velocity of light in a field in the PSA theory, the permittivity of space is defined as

$$\varepsilon = W_0 / W, \tag{35}$$

where W_0 is the initial (free space) energy. Note that the W here is the energy of light in the field which is the total energy minus that shared with the field, i.e.,

$$W = W_0 - 2 w_B. \tag{36}$$

Within gravitational fields, we have
$W = W_0 - (2G\ M\ W_0/r\ c^2)$; where in established cases of 2
$w_B \ll W_0$, or $(2G\ M/rc^2) \ll 1$ as much as

$G\ M\ W_0/r\ c^2$ Joules has left the system of light-mass M and

the other $G\ M\ W_0/r\ c^2$ is shared between the two.

Therefore:

$$\varepsilon = W_0 / \left[W_0 - (2\ G\ M\ W_0/r\ c^2) \right] \text{ or}$$

$$\varepsilon = 1 / \left[1 - (2\ G\ M/r\ c^2) \right]. \tag{37}$$

On the other hand, $\varepsilon = c^2/v^2$ which results in

$$v = c \left[1 - (2\ G\ M/r\ c^2) \right]^{1/2}. \tag{38}$$

For $2\ G\ M/r\ c^2 \ll 1$ we can expand the bracket and keep

only the first order terms. Then we have
$v = c \left[1 - (G\ M/r\ c^2) \right]$ or

$$(c - v)/c = G\ M/r\ c^2. \tag{39}$$

In the case $(2\,G\,M\,/\,r\,c^{\,2}) = 1$, i.e., in a black hole, from Eq. (38) we can see that the speed of light is zero. I claim Eq. (38) gives the speed of light in the field of mass M.

Once we have the wavelength and the speed of light in a field, then from $\lambda\,v = v$ we can find its frequency. From Eqs. (32) and (38) we have

$$v = v_0 \left[\, 1 - (\,2\,w_B\,/\,W_0\,)\,\right]. \qquad (40)$$

Using $w_B = G\,M\,W_0/r\,c^2$ for light in the gravitational field of a mass M, we have

$$v = v_0 \left[\, 1 - (2\,G\,M\,/r\,c^{\,2})\,\right]. \qquad (41)$$

The frequency of light found from Eq. (41) is again valid for all masses M. The frequency of light is zero when $(2G\,M/rc^2) = 1$, i.e., for black holes. Note that once we multiply the two sides of Eq. (41) by Planck's constant "h", we have $hv = h\,v_0 \left[\, 1 - (2\,G\,M\,/rc^2\,)\,\right]$. Since the energy of light is "hν", then we have $W = W_0 \left[1 - (2G\,M/r\,c^2) \right]$ which

is consistent with Eqs. (35) and (37).

One of the many beautiful advantages of the present

model is its physical interpretation of the interaction between

light and fields; e.g., the gravitational fields. One

interpretation of Eq. (36) is that the binding of any light

within the field takes 2 w $_B$ energy away from the energy of

the light, producing a decrease in the frequency and an

increase in the wavelength of the light. According to the PSA

theory, all fields (as well as that of the binding energy) are

E&M waves of different strengths and distributions in nature.

In gravitational fields, inasmuch as $2G\,M\,W_0/rc^2 = 2$ w $_B$ is

taken off the energy of light. Then this energy is given to the

field itself since the field also is of E&M nature. In the

limiting case of black holes, all of the energy of the entering

light or the entering masses is spent on the binding and

sharing with other masses, therefore no light (energy) remains

to be radiated. This is why the energy as well as the

frequency of the radiated light are zero and its wavelength is

infinitely large. Moreover, according to the present model, a black hole is a lump of trapped light, which has radiated part of itself. The remaining part is shared among its components in order to maintain their identity thus making further radiation impossible. Further, it is so much in need of energy that it absorbs all radiation it receives.

Professor Sadegh Angha shows that in fact it is the ε of a space which determines the physical properties of that space.[1] He bases his model of particle production (pair production) on the speed of the advancing γ-ray decreasing (and the permittivity of the space increasing) as it advances toward the center of the static Coulomb field of the electron or the proton. In fact, in the PSA theory the presence of a field in a vacuum (of ε = 1) is the same as the space of different permittivity with no field present. Therefore, it is the permittivity of space, ε, which determines the properties of space. As seen in this section, in the PSA theory the permittivity of space substitutes for the curvature of space. Also, the ε of space determines the quantity of energy (light) an incoming particle (or light) should invest in the field. The investment of energy in a field determines the magnitude of inspiration of the particle itself. Accordingly, the magnitude of inspiration of a particle determines the curvature of space regardless of the apparent type of the field.

32 - MOTION

What is the meaning of motion? The definition of motion has been "the occurrence of displacement in time." In fact, the purpose of mechanics as a branch of science is to study motion. The goal of classical mechanics is to predict the position and velocity of the object at any future time given its initial position and velocity and the forces acting on it. It is obvious therefore that motion is relative. In describing the motion of an object, we must first define a frame of reference with respect to which we make our measurements of the mechanical parameters. Generally speaking, two observers in two different frames of reference (which may be accelerated with respect to each other) describe the motion of an object differently.

One of the principles of Einstein's theory of relativity is that "there is no absolute frame of reference with respect to which the absolute motion of objects are described."[9] This makes perfect sense in our measurements of the physical parameters of objects. In other words, by our definition of motion (i.e., temporal displacement), we have restricted ourselves to the relativity of our measurements.

Within the context of the PSA theory, I have repeatedly discussed the radiation energy trapped in an object or in a particle. For a particle moving in a space free of any field with constant speed "v", the radiation energy is $m_0 v^2 / \left[1 - (v^2/c^2) \right]^{1/2}$.[1] For a particle moving in a field, the total radiation energy is 2 w_B. The binding energy, which would have left the particle, is now trapped in the particle and acts as the kinetic energy of the particle. For a stationary particle in a field, the kinetic energy has been radiated as the binding energy. However, in our treatment of this particle we still have to consider the total radiation energy as 2 w $_B$. I will discuss this in more detail later in this section.

Here I will try to define my definition of the motion of a particle or an object: *The content of motion of any object is the amount of radiation i.e. light, it has or shares with a field or with other particles.*

In the PSA theory of particle structure, Professor Sadegh Angha proposes an explanation for the fact that the speed of light is constant in a vacuum.[1] Considering light in a vacuum does not invest energy in any field, the permittivity of the environment stays constant ($\varepsilon = 1$). This is also the case for light in free space (no investment in any field) regardless of the inertial frame of reference used for observation. Thus all observers in all inertial frames agree that the light has not invested in any field, and consequently it has a speed of $c = 3 \times 10^{8}$ m/s. This principle of relativity therefore, becomes a natural consequence of PSA's theory. We also accept the other principle of relativity which states that "all inertial frames are equivalent with respect to all laws of physics." Having established this, all of the equations of the special theory of relativity are applicable for PSA's theory of a particle moving with a velocity "v".

The advantage of the above definition of motion lies in the fact that now "motion" is not restricted to displacement, but is characteristic of the radiation content of a system. Even systems in a field not actually being displaced with respect to an observer are characterized by motion with respect to that observer's frame of reference. Although these systems are stationary within their own frames of reference, they contain motion with respect to an observer (stationary) outside the field because they share some radiation with the field and thus can be assumed to be moving with respect to this observer.

The "rest" penetration radius (ρ_0) which is the radius beyond which particle has "matter" structure[1] and the "in-field rest mass" (μ_0) can be found through Eqs. (17) and (18);

i.e., $\rho_0 = r_0 \Big/ \Big[1 - (2\,w_B/W_0)\Big]^{1/2}$ and $\mu_0 = m_0\Big[1 - (2\,w_B/W_0)\Big]^{1/2}$. All transformation equations of special relativity are applicable to these systems as well. In fact, we can find the "fictitious" speed of an observer outside the field with respect to the stationary system in the field by assuming $\Big[1- (2\,w_B/W_0)\Big]^{1/2} = \Big[1-(v_f^2/c^2)\Big]^{1/2}$ where the subscript "f" of v_f stands for "fictitious". From the above Eq. we have $v_f = (2w_B/m_0)^{1/2}$. This is the reason why "time" and "space"

in different strength fields (e.g., different strengths of gravitational fields) are especially different. Einstein related this difference of space-time to the different geometric (curvatures) of space-time. Here a particle at rest in a field can be treated as a particle moving with a constant speed. Therefore the transformation equations of special relativity can be applied. To briefly summarize, a system which shares

part of its "rest" energy (as measured by an observer) with a

field, contains "motion" and has therefore either lost some of

its rest mass or alternatively, its penetration radius has

increased.

For the case where $\left[\ 1 - (\ 2\ w_B / W_0\ )\ \right]^{1/2} = 0,$

i.e.,

$$2\ w_B = W_0 = m_0 c^2, \qquad (42)$$

all of the "rest" energy of the system has converted into

radiation energy. For this system there is no "matter" left to

be shared to produce more radiation. Thus no more binding

energy is radiated out of this system. This system in fact is

frozen in time and space; its structure is frozen light in space.

Since light itself is timeless, the above system must be frozen

in both time and space. *I claim this system (which in the case*

of gravitational fields is a gravitational black hole) is in the

state of absolute rest. Clearly in the case of gravitational

fields, the reference frame of a black hole is an absolute frame of reference. Taking a system entirely made of motion as a system in absolute rest may seem contradictory. However, it should be noted that this motion (i.e. this system) is in a frozen state both with respect to time and space. This frozen state is the state of absolute rest.

33 - THE INSPIRATION OF THE UNIVERSE.

Most people have heard of "the expansion of the universe." This hypothesis has been developed in response to the discovery of redshift (Doppler shift) in the spectrum of light received from distant stars and galaxies.[6] On the basis of these spectroscopic measurements, astronomers concluded that most galaxies are moving away from each other. This is demonstrated by the spectrum of light emitted from these galaxies being shifted to the longer (red) wavelength. Hubble showed the speed of a galaxy is proportional to its distance from us. This is known as the Hubble law and is expressed as $n = HD$. Here n is the speed of the galaxy in km/sec, D is the distance in Mpc (1 Mpc = 3.09 X 10^{19} km) and H is the Hubble constant (in km/sec. Mpc). Although the exact value of H is not yet agreed upon, a value of 75 km/sec. Mpc seems to be most widely accepted.[6] In order to find an approximate value for the age of the universe, we assume that in the beginning, the earth and all the galaxies were together. Assuming the speed of the galaxies has been constant, the time to travel a distance Δ for a galaxy then can be calculated from the Hubble equation (n = HD). In essence $T = (\Delta/H \Delta)$ or $T = 1/H$. The substitution of the numerical value of the Hubble constant results in $T = 4.12 \times 10^{17}$ sec = 13 billion years. Assuming the universe has been expanding with the speed of light, then the approximate distance of the earth to the edge of the universe is 13 billion Light Years (= 1.2324 X 10^{26} km, 1 LY = 9.48 X 10^{12} km).[6]

A widely accepted theory of the origin of the universe is the Big Bang theory. On the basis of Einstein's general relativistic cosmological equations, Abbe Georges Lamaitre suggested that the observed universe was originally very hot and dense and expanded explosively. However, George Gamow suggested the present version of the Big Bang theory in the 1940's.[5] At the earliest stages of the Big Bang (10^{-4} sec after the start) the universe was very hot (about 10^{12} K). As the universe expanded, the temperature dropped and after 24 sec the temperature was $T = 5 \times 10^{9}$ K. After 34 minutes of expansion, the temperature dropped to $T = 3 \times 10^{8}$ K. After a few hundred thousand years, the temperature was T =

300 K. The expansion continues today. Scientists believe that the background (the Big Bang residual) temperature of the universe should be about 3 K. This has been experimentally confirmed, and measurement has resulted in a background temperature of 2.7 K.[6]

How does the universe expand? Is there no outside limit for the universe? And as the universe expands, is space-time "created"? Is it possible for something to be born out of nothing? Professor Sadegh Angha says, " nonexistence does not exist and existence is united." *It is my belief that the expansion of the universe must take place within some existing being.* In order to introduce this medium, let me begin with the present time universe, especially the internal structure of particles.

According to PSA's theory,[1] a particle is the same as its field. For every particle, especially, there is a penetration radius where the observable field stops. Professor Sadegh Angha discusses the structure of the inside of the penetration sphere and suggests that there is a black hole inside the penetration sphere of each particle.[1] Let us investigate the possibility of this model. In section 9 we saw that in order to have a black hole, a mass (or particle) must have shared all of its mass and converted it to radiation energy. In essence, we must have the condition $2 w_B = W_0 = m_0 c^2$. Part of the shared radiation energy leaves the system while the trapped part attracts radiation in order to free the components of the system from one another. If the energy of the incoming radiation is too insignificant to free a component from the bondage of the others, it could nevertheless excite the system to a higher energy level. Conversely, for a particle, which has not shared any part of itself with other fields, or particles, all of the rest energy is present; this particle therefore does not attract any radiation. Even if we place our frames of reference at radii close to the penetration radius of the particle, the radiation energy remains zero. This is true because the radiation energy is independent of where the frame of reference is just so long as it is stationary with respect to the particle. Therefore the wavelength $\lambda = \lambda_0 / \left[1 - (2 w_B / W'_0) \right]^{1/2}$ is not redshifted. Notice W_0 is replaced by W'_0 because it is the rest mass measured by the observer who has advanced toward the penetration radius of the particle. This W_0' is equal to $e^2/2\ r_0 - e^2/2\ r$ where "r" is

the radius at the location of the observer. In other words, the

observer sees only that part of the particle on which he

himself is located. The observer who is exactly located at the

penetration radius (r_0), sees no part of the particle and thus

his measurement is $W_0' = 0$. At this point it can be speculated

that

$$\frac{2\ W_B}{W_0'} = 1 \tag{43}$$

This is the case because for all "r" we have no radiation

energy, i.e., $w_B = 0$, and thus $2w_B \leq W_0'$. Also at the

penetration radius $W_0' = 0$, the two terms $2\ w_B$ and W_0' are

zeros of the same order. Therefore at the penetration radius of

a particle, $\lambda \left\{ = \lambda_0 \Big/ \left[1 - (2\ w_B / W_0')\right]^{1/2} \right\} \to \infty$,

meaning the realm of a black hole starts. In essence, $\lambda \to \infty$

means no information from inside a particle can reach an

observer. At the penetration radius, the permittivity of space

is infinity $\left\{ \epsilon(r_0) = 1 \Big/ \left[1-(2\ w_B/W_0)\right] \to \infty \right\}$ for the

penetrating field of the particle itself. Once radiation energy (kinetic energy) is given to the particle, ε (r_0) changes to a finite value for the new particle. Again ε becomes infinite at the new penetration radius of Eq. (19). The black hole inside the particle extends from the penetration radius to the center of the particle. As a result of the injection of light (or kinetic energy) into a particle, the relative motion of the particle from one point to another takes place as (spiral) redistribution of energy around different points (black holes) of space. This is because the black hole inside the penetration sphere is penetrable only with more energy. In other words, during translational motion of a particle the penetration spheres of the particle do not translate. This means that actually existence does not move from one place to another; rather the manifestations redistribute their energy, much like the ocean waves.

What is the nature of this black hole? As I stated earlier, a black hole is basically trapped light, i.e., all particles of a black hole have shared all of themselves with other particles and have radiated the binding energy. Therefore only the remaining shared light remains in the system. To reiterate, when masses combine, they emit part of their shared radiation; the other part remains in the system to maintain the energy distribution of the component particles. This trapped radiation which remains seeks the lost part in order to free the particles from one another's bond. For a black hole all of the rest energy of the particles ($W_0 = m_0 c^2$) has been shared in the form of full radiation. Part of that radiation has left the system and the other part is trapped in search of the lost half. The structure of a black hole therefore is all trapped radiation or light. Because this lump of light needs to capture its lost part, every light is absorbed by it. It should be noted that every part, or particle, of a black hole is itself a black hole. This means that for every particle of a black hole the equation $W_0 = 2 w_B$ holds. However, being a lump of trapped radiation, a black hole also represents a single unit. In addition, it is important to note that the distribution of the needed energy around every point of the black hole is (approximately) e $^2/2$ r. This is true because this is the distribution of the energy of the interacting particles and also it is equal to half of the distribution of the shared radiation energy. Therefore in its penetration, a radiation wave (e.g., a γ-ray) takes the same energy distribution. A black hole then is a radiation field of negative energy with a "microscopic" distribution of energy of - $e^2/2r$.

At the edge of the universe, the frontier of the universe - which is light - advances into the black hole of *nihility*. Here, for the first time ever, I claim that the universe itself is within a black hole. It has been born, and is advancing into this black hole. Since the big bang itself, the γ-ray photons at the edge of the universe have been absorbed into the black hole, have matched it, compensated the lost binding energy, and have released twice as much total energy in the form of particles or antiparticles. Some of these particles-antiparticles undergo pair annihilation and then regenerate more of γ-ray photons. This has provided the γ-ray photons to be absorbed further into the black hole. Note that the process of doubling the energy involves a chain reaction that provides the energy necessary for a vaster area of the edge of the universe.

The expansion of the universe takes place as the black hole surrounding the universe swallows the γ-ray radiation and a particle or antiparticle is created. The energy distribution of a particle or an antiparticle is around a point of this black hole. The distribution of energy around any point of the black hole is $+e^2/2r$ down to the penetration radius of the particle or antiparticles and $-e^2/2r$ from the penetration sphere to the inside down to the center. The space is filled with these tiny black holes which I call *"the point black holes"*, around which the particles have spiral distribution. As soon as one particle distributes itself around another point black hole, some other particle replaces it. This forms the particles' displacement, which is basically nothing but redistribution of the particles around different point black holes of the universe.

Essentially, the pattern of the particle structure exists inside the black hole surrounding the universe - which I call *"heavens black hole."* This means the incoming γ-ray penetrates as far as the penetration radius of the particle. Therefore, I claim that the pattern of the structure of the universe has existed before the universe was created around the helical penetrated black hole which now resides at the center of each elementary particle as well as at the frontier of the universe. In my opinion, ***ether***^{2} is basically this black hole around which energy is distributed helically to form the visible universe. Inasmuch as the heaven black hole inhales the γ-ray photons, and as a result of that the universe expands I call this inhalation *the inspiration of the universe.*

34 - THE RESPIRATION THEORY, THE UNIFIED REPRESENTATION OF BEING

In previous sections, I discussed the expansion or contraction of particles, atoms, molecules, macroscopic objects, the earth, the sun and the universe. I referred to this expansion as the breathing of these objects. I also derived the equations of the penetration radius of a free particle participating in a field (e.g. a gravitational field) as a function of the field strength. In derivation of the equations of the penetration radii, the type of the field did not affect the general equations.

We can show that all of the macroscopic and microscopic dynamic variables of a particle will be known once the expansion and/or the contraction in the penetration radius is given. The latter refers to the particle's nuclear, atomic, molecular, or gravitational domain of interaction. The purpose of identifying the domain of interaction is to know the functional form of the binding energy.

Let us begin with the investigation of the gravitational domain of interaction of a particle. Professor Sadegh Angha has shown that the particle and the gravitational field with which it is interacting both share the same amount of radiation energy. Therefore, classically, half of the total shared energy leaves the system. Classically, both the particle and the field share as much as w_B of energy. The particle stores the total radiation energy inside itself and initially speeds up towards the center of the gravitational field. Thus, the radiation energy of the particle is $M v^2 = 2 w_B$. In order to find the new penetration radius of the particle, we follow the same procedures as before. We assume the wavelength of the new particle at the radius where the radiation energy starts (R) to be the same as that at r_0. In that case we have $\lambda = \lambda_0 \Rightarrow$ $(h/e)(2R/M)^{1/2} = (h/e)(2r_0/m_0)^{1/2}$ where M is the "moving" mass of the particle. Considering $Mc^2 = e^2/2 R_0$ and $m_0 c^2 = e^2/2 r_0$ we have

$$R = \frac{r_0^{\,2}}{R_0} \tag{45}$$

The radiation energy should occupy the space inside the particle from the radius R down to R_0. Thus we have

$$\frac{e^2}{2R_0} - \frac{e^2}{2R} = M v^2 \tag{46}$$

Using Eq. (45) in Eq. (46) we have $(e^2/2 R_0)(1 - R_0^2/r_0^2) = M v^2$. Then we have $M c^2 (1 - R_0^2/r_0^2) = M v^2$ which results in $(1 - R_0^2/r_0^2) = (v^2/c^2)$ or:

$$R_0 = r_0 \left[1 - (v^2/c^2) \right]^{1/2}, \tag{47}$$

therefore the familiar result derived in the PSA theory and that of special relativity.[1] Equation (47) results in

$$M = \frac{m_0}{\left[1 - (v^2/c^2) \right]^{1/2}} \tag{48}$$

Using Eqs. (45) and (47) the radius R is

$$R = \frac{r_0}{\left[1 - (v^2/c^2) \right]^{1/2}} \tag{49}$$

From the above equation, it can be seen that the radiation energy penetrates from both sides of r_0 once some energy (in this case matching with the field) is injected inside the particle. The kinetic energy of the particle extends from r_0 to R_0 and the rest of the radiation energy fills the space of the particle from the radius R down to r_0. Let us calculate the energy of the particle from r_0 to R_0. This energy is equal to $(e^2/2R_0)$-$(e^2/2r_0)$. Again, considering $(e^2/2R_0) = M c^2$ and $(e^2/2r_0) = m_0 c^2$, we have $(e^2/2R_0) - (e^2/2r_0) = M c^2 - m_0 c^2$ which is the relativistic kinetic energy. The energy from the r_0 to R is $(e^2/2r_0) - (e^2/2R)$. Using Eq. (49), we arrive at

$$(e^2/2r_0) - (e^2/2R) = (e^2/2r_0) - (e^2/2r_0)\left[1 -(v^2/c^2) \right]^{1/2} =$$
$$m_0 c^2 \left\{ 1-\left[1-(v^2/c^2) \right]^{1/2} \right\}. \tag{50}$$

On the other hand, we have

$$M v^2 - KE = M v^2 - M c^2 + m_0 c^2.$$

Using Eq. (48) for M we have

$$Mv^2 - KE = m_0 c^2 \left\{ 1 -\left[1 - (v^2/c^2) \right]^{1/2} \right\}. \tag{51}$$

The right hand sides of the Eqs. (50) and (51) are the same. Thus

$$(e^2/2r_0) - (e^2/2R) = M v^2 - KE. \qquad (52)$$

Consequently, the energy of the particle between the radii r_0 and R is equal to the total radiation energy minus the kinetic energy.

Once the particle is stationary in a gravitational field, its total energy is $m_0 c^2$ and the radiation energy is $M v^2 = 2 w_B$. It is true that the KE which is the same as w_B in the classical cases of $w_B \ll m_0 c^2$ is already radiated out of the system of the particle-field. However, since there has to be an empty place for the missing energy, the particle behaves as if the total radiation energy is $2 w_B$ so that the lost w_B can be sought. In other words, when the particles match gravitationally and radiate w_B, the lack of this energy must be registered in the system; otherwise the particles have no reason to seek the lost energy. Therefore the system has to behave as if the total radiation energy includes the lost part so that, when available, this energy is absorbed. Always when one of the masses is much bigger than the other (e.g., the earth and the sun), the radiation energy is stored in the smaller component. This is because the bigger object practically remains stationary and the smaller object is displaced. The penetration radius of the unmatched part of the particle and its mass are given by Eqs. (17) and (18), i.e. $\rho_0 = R = r_0 / \left[1 - (2w_B/W_0) \right]^{1/2}$ and $\mu_0 = m_0 \left[1 - (2 \ w_B \ / \ W_0) \right]^{1/2}$, respectively. The radiation energy left in the system extends from the spheres of radii ρ_0 ($= R$) and r_0. This energy is

$$(e^2/2r_0) - (e^2/2\rho_0) = m_0 \ c^2 \left[1 - r_0/\rho_0 \right] = W_0 \left\{ 1 - \left[1 - (2 \ w_B / W_0) \right]^{1/2} \right\}, \tag{53}$$

which is $M \ v^2$ - KE where for a stationary particle inside a field KE is the lost kinetic energy. Note that for $w_B \ll m_0 \ c^2 = W_0$, we can expand the $\left[1 - (2 \ w_B / W_0) \right]^{1/2}$ term and keep only the term up to the first order in $(2 \ w_B / W_0)$. In that case: $(e^2/2r_0)$ - $(e^2/2\rho_0)$ = w $_B$. Thus, in the classical

case of w$_B$ $\ll$ m$_0$c^2, the radiation energy stored in a

stationary particle in a field is the same as w $_B$, meaning the

lost kinetic energy is the same as w $_B$ itself. But, in the other

extreme, where 2 w $_B$ $\approx$ m$_0$ c^2 ,this left over energy is

approximately equal to m$_0$ c ^{2} = W$_0$ itself. This means that

for a black hole the entire particle has been converted to

radiation energy and the binding energy is also captured by

the black hole itself.

Now let us look at the case of a charged particle

entering an opposite electric field. Again, the matching of the

particle with the field produces radiation, which is partially

used to accelerate the particle. The particle and the field each

share the same amount of energy, which is equal to w $_B$ at

any "r" from the center of the field. Thus, the total radiation

energy is M v ^{2} = 2 w $_B$ at any point. Again, the new

penetration radius and mass of the now moving particle are

given by Eqs. (47) and (48), respectively. The advancement

of the radiation energy is again continued to a radius R that is

given by Eq. (49). The kinetic energy of the particle extends from r_0 to R_0 and the remainder of the radiation energy is spread in the space from R to r_0. We can show this exactly in the same way as in the case of gravitational interaction. The penetration radius and the mass of the matter part of the particle are given by Eqs. (17) and (18).

The case of a charged particle in a repulsive field is different. In this case to bring the charge to the point "r" from the center of the field $2\,w_B$ of energy must be *invested*. This energy "sews" the particle to the field so that they no longer repel each other. To bring the particle even closer to the center of the field, more energy is needed for binding to occur. In fact, according to the PSA theory of the neutron, the particle neutron is nothing but one half of the "sewing" energy necessary to bind two protons to one another.[1] This sewing energy is in the form of "full" radiation energy and is distributed within the space of the particle. Furthermore, it does not increase or decrease the penetration radius of the particle. Once the particle is free to move, the sewing energy enters itself into the penetration sphere of the stationary particle and the particle is accelerated. The time rate of this penetration (the acceleration) depends on how much matching radiation energy remains in the space of the particle outside the new penetration sphere, ρ_0. When all energy outside the last penetration radius (ρ_0) is depleted, the acceleration process stops, and the speed of the particle remains constant. The penetration radius of the new particle (the moving mass) and the penetration radius of the unmatched part of the particle can be found through Eqs. (47) and (49), respectively. The kinetic energy is the energy between the radii r_0 and R_0, and the rest of the radiation energy ($M v^2$ - KE) lies between the radii R and r_0.

From the equations presented thus far it is apparent that once we have the penetration radii of the particle (either R_0 or R for a moving particle or ρ_0 for a stationary particle in a field) we can find both its speed and its moving mass. The radiation energy W ($= M v^2$) can then be calculated using the latter two parameters. The knowledge of the radiation energy (or the motion of the particle) is then sufficient to set up the PSA wave equation[1]

$$\nabla^2 \, \xi(\vec{r}) + (W \, W_0 / \hbar^2 c^2) \, \xi(\vec{r}) = 0. \tag{54}$$

Here $\xi(\vec{r}) = \vec{r} . \vec{E}$ or $\vec{r} . \vec{B}$, with $\vec{E}$ and $\vec{B}$ being the electric field and magnetic field distribution of the radiation energy of the particle, and W_0 the rest energy of the particle.[1] According to Prof. Sadegh Angha, the time variation of $\xi(\vec{r},$ t) and consequently, that of

$\vec{E}(\vec{r}, t)$ and $\vec{B}(\vec{r}, t)$ is shown by

$$\xi(\vec{r}, t) = \xi(\vec{r}) \, e^{i \omega t}, \tag{55}$$

where $\xi(\vec{r})$ is the solution to the PSA wave equation (53) and

$$W = \hbar \omega = M v^2. \tag{56}$$

Therefore, the electromagnetic field of the "motion" (i.e., radiation energy) of the particle is temporally a monochromatic wave. The speed of this wave is the same as its phase velocity. Being of single frequency, this wave will

not spread in time. Let us calculate the phase velocity of this

wave. The phase velocity of a wave is $v_p = \omega/k$ where "k"

is the wave vector. Since $k = \vec{P}/\hbar$, where $\vec{P}$ is the momentum

of the particle, then using Eq. (56), we have $v_p = M v^2/P$

with P being the magnitude of the momentum vector $\vec{P}$. On

the other hand $\vec{P} = M \vec{v}$; therefore

$$v_p = v = \left[1 - (R_0^{\,2}/r_0^{\,2}) \right]^{1/2} c, \qquad (57)$$

where I have used Eq. (47) in the derivation of the right hand

side of Eq. (57). Equation (57) expresses the fact that the

phase velocity of the propagation of the motion (or the

radiation energy of the particle) is the same as its mechanical

velocity. Although Eq. (57) is merely a scalar equation, I

generalize it to a vector equation. The material part of the

particle, therefore, travels with the same velocity as that of the

propagation of the radiation energy. Being a monochromatic

wave, the E&M field of the particle's motion will exist at all

times. In essence, since the absolute value of a sine or cosine wave is always less than one, the time variation of the motion of the particle will remain limited, even for $t \to \infty$. The frequency of this motion will not change unless the magnitude of the radiation energy of the particle changes and that happens only when the speed of the particle changes. This is another way of expressing Newton's first law of motion.

The total energy of the particle is $M c^2$. As previously demonstrated, the distribution of the radiation energy in the particle is from radius R_0 to R. This energy has the form

$$W = (e^2/2 R_0) - (e^2/2R) = M c^2(1 - R_0/R).   (58)$$

Inserting this in Eq. (54) and changing R to r (to indicate the variable nature of R), we have

$$\nabla^2 \xi(\vec{r}) + \left[M^2 c^2 (1 - R_0/r)/\hbar^2 \right] \xi(\vec{r}) = 0,   (59)$$

which is a differential equation solved by the method of separation of variables. Note that r (= R) is where the radiation energy of the "new" particle starts. Appendix I shows the solution $\xi(\vec{r})$ to equation (59), as well as the equations which derive the $\vec{E}$ and $\vec{B}$ field from this solution. This E & M field of the radiation then will give the dynamic variables of the radiation energy or that of the particle. Since $\varepsilon = W_0/W$ then using Eq. (58) we have

$$\varepsilon = (1 - R_0/r)^{-1}. \tag{60}$$

For the case of a stationary particle in a field, we have

$$W_0 = m_0 c^2,$$

$$W = (e^2/2r_0) - (e^2/2\rho_0) = m_0 c^2 (1 - r_0/\rho_0), \tag{61}$$

and

$$\varepsilon = (1 - r_0/\rho_0)^{-1}. \tag{62}$$

Defining r to represent ρ_0; for the case of a stationary particle in a field the term $\left[m_0^2 c^2 (1 - r_0/r)/\hbar^2 \right]$ must be substituted for $\left[M^2 c^2 (1 - R_0/r)/\hbar^2 \right]$ in Eq. (59).

In the expressions of the E&M field of the particle there are two appropriate parameters. These parameters are A, which is a constant, and ℓ, the intrinsic angular momentum of this radiation. The energy and the momentum of radiation of a particle are found through

$$W = (1/16\,\pi) \int (\mathcal{E}\,\vec{E}\,^*.\,\vec{E} + \vec{B}\,.\,\vec{B}\,^*)\,dV, \qquad (63)$$

$$\vec{P} = (1/8\,\pi c) \int (\mathcal{E}\,\vec{E} \times \vec{B}\,^*)\,dV, \qquad (64)$$

where the integrals are over the volume between the spheres of radii R_0 and R, and the symbol "*" indicates the complex conjugate of the fields. Equation (64) gives the magnitude as well as the direction of the momentum of this radiation (or particle). On the other hand, since the magnitude of the radiation energy and momentum are $W = M\,v^2$ and $\vec{P} = M\,\vec{v}$, respectively, then the above equations can be used to find the fitting parameters A and ℓ. The extrinsic angular momentum of the radiation (or particle) is found through

$$\vec{L} = (1/8\,\pi\,c) \int \mathcal{E}\left[\vec{r}\,X(\vec{E}\,X\,\vec{B})\right]\,dV \qquad (65)$$

which gives the direction of the vector of angular momentum as well as its magnitude. We can find all of the dynamic variables of the particle through the E&M field of its radiation.

In summary, as presented in this section, the macroscopic and microscopic dynamic parameters of the "motion" of a particle (whose r_0 is known) can be derived once the penetration radius, R_0 or R (or ρ_0) is given. This is true no matter which interaction of the particle is being investigated. In essence, to determine the dynamic variables of a particle, so long as the penetration radius of the particle is given, the type of the field is immaterial. Since it is the magnitude of expansion/contraction of the penetration radius of the particle which is important, I call this theory *the respiration theory*. The respiration model is in reality a unified scheme presenting the particle interaction in all fields.

For more than 40 years physicists have searched for a unified scheme of representation of the fields. Perhaps

Einstein was the first physicist who proposed the geometry of space as a candidate for such a scheme. However, his as well as those of his successors' attempts to present the fields as curvature of space have been in vain. The respiration theory represents the culmination of this effort.

35 - Professor Angha's Guidance and Conclusions.

It was because of Professor Sadegh Angha's work that I have been inspired and pulled to the foregoing mathematical approaches and models. As Isaac Newton said, "if I can see afar, it is because I am on the shoulder of giants." Contrary to what Thomas Edison claimed, that "genius is one percent inspiration and 99 percent perspiration", in this revolutionary research it has been my good fortune to have been inspired 99 percent of the time by my father's work and teachings. In this presentation I have only touched a shallow part of Professor Sadegh Angha's ideas. I postpone a more detailed investigation of his ideas to a future time when the present work is understood and, where possible, experimentally verified. I will, however, mention here some of his verses and poems, which have both inspired and directed me in the present work.

In The Epic of Life, he writes:[10]

1-   *The primordial wisdom, the source of traits, created thousands of manifestations from **nihility**.*

2-   In the beginning the physical matter received life
       through divine **inspiration**.

3-   Under the command of the ancient, the particle
       journeyed within particles.

4-   Everything was borne out of one once the **breath**
       of truth blew into the skies.

5-   The fact that the universe became alive by one
       breath is not obvious except to God.

6-   The possible manifestations are not the truth but the
       motion of **breath** is. The life of breath is the essence
       of the united.

7-   An **expiration** moved through the heart of material
       particles thereby the human was born in this righteous
       creation.

8-   Through each **breath** the wave becomes the
       particle. Then the wave-particles manifest.

9-   In truth, a droplet is the sea itself. In truth a particle
       is the sun itself.

10-   If you broaden your vision of the universe and journey
       from the end to the beginning, you will see that love

has created the universe just like the links which make the chain.

11-   *Once love filled the heart of the universe, wisdom became drunk from the strength of this wine.*

12-   *To say love gave life to the two universes is the same as to say existence appeared from the essence.*

13-   *The definition of creation of the universe is: "motion" from "motion" in "motion".*

14-   *The story book of the universe of creations is wrapped between two nihilities.*

15-   *In the horizon of existence, and with every inspiration/expiration, the oscillation of a wave draws the sketch of manifestation.*

16-   *Once the circle of the particle is borne of light, the universe celebrates anew.*

17-   *Colors are manifestations of the colorless. Particles and waves are the same in truth.*

18-   *A wave is from field and particles are from a wave.*

19-   *A wave converts to particles.*

20-   *The manifestation of a wave is material particles then the particle attracts each particle.*

21-   *The universe became excited once the wave formed particles.*

22-   *The wave has put on the disguise of particles then it acts in objects, plants, and life.*

23-   *The ocean of unity is manifest in creation through the wave.*

In <u>The Principles of Faghr and Sufism</u> he writes:[11]

"In the background of the active realm of the human's natural senses, he perceives the heavens as moving. Therefore he seeks the beginning and the end of this journey. He wants to understand all of the characteristics of these motions. In this endeavor sometimes he looks for the cause of motion and other times he confuses motion with the spatial and temporal reflections of the objects. ...

... In their study of the journey of "motion" physicists have stopped at merely considering the moving objects and investigate only the temporal manifestations of the vast entity of "motion". ...

... The human being becomes amazed and sometimes confused by the mysterious arrangement of the particles and their different motions. The human's imagination is naturally in need of temporally arranging the reflections it receives. Only when these temporal arrangements make their sense in his perception does he look for their final cause. ...

... In the definition of motion I say: first, motion in its essence does not belong to anything; second in its trait it is always giving; third, it is in no way a limited entity and thus it cannot be known through its manifestations. ...

... Human imagination has confused the "motion" itself with the moving body. Motion has its own independent meaning and characteristic. Motion does not have annihilating and damping characteristics. Thus, it does not have a beginning and an end. It is the cause, not an effect. Displacement is its final manifestation, not its essence. ...

... The human being has studied the effects of motion. Motion itself is the essence of all objects. ...

... During any transformational manifestation the essence of motion is undisturbed. ...

...Einstein says, "we cannot perceive absolute motion". This is because we have limited our observations to the three dimensional physical world. This world is a creation of the human's limited mental power. If we knew the essence of motion then we would know that motion itself is nothing but absolute. ...

... The translational motion of the object is in fact an indication of their ability to accept the gravitational (or the attractive) field coordinates. This ability is relative. Yet the essence of the objects (or motion) does not go through any transformation. ...

... The perception of the human senses is nothing but the creations of the senses themselves. ...

... The main reason why the researchers cannot understand the truth of objects is because they themselves are separated from the essence of the object. What the researcher perceives from the object is merely the shallow layers of the essence of the object.

... In, Az Janin Ta Janan (From the Womb to the Heavens) Lord Mir Ghotbeddin Mohammad Angha says:[12] *"The space is full of ether, which we call the etheric fluid. The absolute*

energy is the essence of motion and motion itself has produced the essence of particles, which in turn are the foundations of the universe. Motion manifests as different particles and eventually as different objects. In all these different manifestations the entity of motion is identical."...

In <u>Chanteh (The Gnostic's Cosmos)</u> he says:[13]

1- *Whatever you see in nature (from small to large) was in nihility, then it came into existence.*

2- *If you find the way to the secrets of nihility, then you will find the bare secret of existence. This is the grand way.*

3- *Nihility is the ocean of the generosity of truth. In fact, it is not nihility, but it is the absolute existence.*

4- *Every moment existence emerges from nihility. Thus the eternal existence is hidden in our nihility.*

5- *The wave is one wave, not many waves.*

6- *All manifestations, transformations, and changes are the journeys of force but not separated from it. Light or matter are the journeys of force.*

7-   *Matter is energy and force; it has the same substance as energy.*

8-   *Nihility is like a mirror reflecting the essence of truth.*

9-   *With its every inspiration, nihility draws the sketch of small and large.*

10-   *In truth the existence is an inspiration. The secret of inspiration is the rule for the appearance of the universe.*

In conclusion, I have attempted to show that all things, from a particle to the universe itself, breathe. The life and the living activity of the cosmos, the birth of new systems out of old ones, all is maintained by the breathing of the components. New nuclei are born through the breathing of old ones. Two nuclei combine or collide to produce a new, heavier nucleus in a process called nuclear fusion. In fusion, the component protons and neutrons inspire. Any exchange of energy among the atoms, molecules, or more complex systems produces a change in the penetration radius of component atoms. The fusion of the H nuclei in the core of the sun combined with the gravitational attraction of the components of the core results in an oscillation of the core or the whole sun. The formation of the stars or galaxies - under the effect of gravitation - leads to a change in the penetration radius of the component atoms. This is gravitational breathing. In the limiting case of gravitational inspiration, all of the particles have shared their matter parts and the only energy present in the system is in the form of trapped radiation energy. In that case the star has converted to a black hole. Our value for the radius beyond which no radiation can escape the black hole matches that found through intricate calculations of general relativity. Also our value of the redshift agrees with that found through general relativistic calculations.

I redefined the concept of motion. This new definition expresses that the radiation energy content of a particle is the content of the motion of that particle. In this context particles which are stationary but have participated in a field are considered moving. The frame of reference of a stationary particle in a field can be considered as an inertial frame with a constant relative fictitious speed. Thus the transformation equations of special relativity can be applied to such a reference frame.

Our universe has been expanding within a giant gravitational black hole. At the edge of the universe the γ-ray photons propagates into the black hole (of nihility) and frees particles and antiparticles; some of which rejoin and produce γ-ray photons again. This process is a chain reaction and consequently provides fuel for the expanding universe. The spiral of a particle is around a tiny black hole. I call this the point black hole. Professor Sadegh Angha says there are two nihilities and manifestations of being that occur between these two.

Finally, I presented Prof. Sadegh Angha's Inspiration Theory. The amount of inspiration/expiration of a particle is sufficient information to determine the dynamic variables of a particle. After solving the PSA wave equation for the radiation energy of the particle, I derived its $\overrightarrow{\mathbf{E}}$ and $\overrightarrow{\mathbf{B}}$ field; and demonstrated that fitting parameters can be found. I then showed that the time variation of the E&M field is a monochromatic wave and that the phase velocity of this wave

is the same as the mechanical velocity of the particle. Thus the particle's wave does not expand or contract in time.

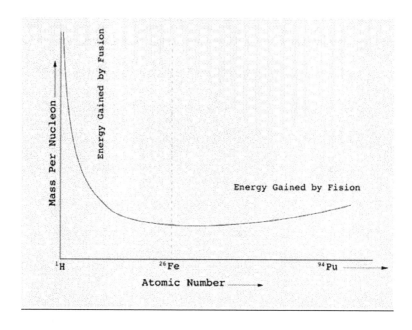

Figure 1- A schematic of mass per nucleon versus the atomic number. For nuclei less massive than Fe, the mass per nucleon decreases as the atomic number increases. Conversely, for those nucleons more massive than Fe, the mass per nucleon increases as the atomic number increases. The scale is arbitrary.

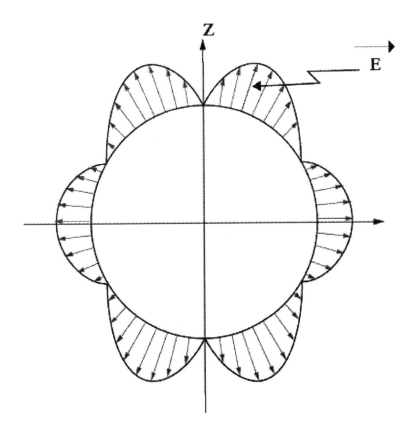

Figure 2- A schematic of θ variation of $\vec{E_r}$, of the proton for r = constant $\gg r_0$ (= e $^2/m_0$ c^2) and $\phi = \pi/2$ and 3 $\pi/2$ planes. The outward direction of the vectors indicates the positivity of $\vec{E_r}$. The scale is arbitrary.

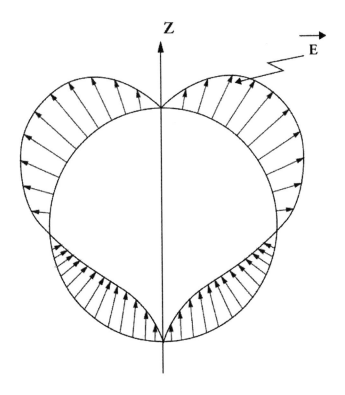

Figure 3- A schematic of θ variation of $\vec{E}_r$, of the neutron for r = constant $\gg r_0$ (= e ^{2} /m$_0$c ^{2}) and $\phi = \pi/2$ and 3 $\pi/2$ planes. The variable r is taken such that the r dependence of $\vec{E}_r$ is positive. The scale is arbitrary.

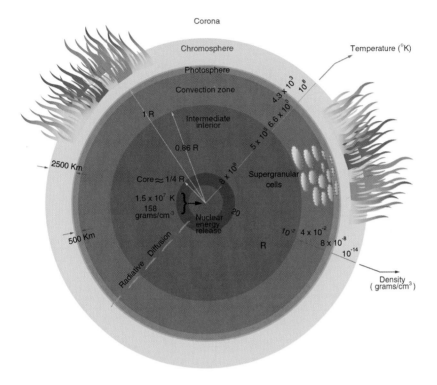

Figure 4- A schematic of the sun. Among other things, the theoretical values of the temperature as well as those of the density at different layers are mentioned.

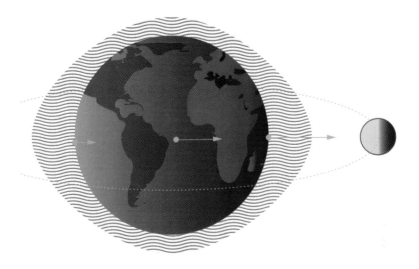

Figure 6 - A schematic of the tidal effect of the moon on the earth. Relative to the center of the earth, the near side and the far side are pulled outwards.

CHAPTER 4

HUMAN BREATHING AND
CONCENTRATION

36 - INTRODUCTION

The goal of scientific research is to discover the laws of nature and help us to better understand ourselves and live more in harmony with our environment and thus, the universe as a whole. Following this pattern, the advent of cold fusion as the main source of energy and the paramount energy regulator in our body necessitates a detailed investigation of the magnitude of this phenomenon in our lives. In chapters one and two I discussed the effects of cold fusion in our physical life and health. In this chapter I will move forward and investigate the effects of cold fusion in our mental life and health. I will discuss the physiological mechanism of concentration, the characteristic role of cold fusion in concentration and the levels of concentration.

In light of this endeavor, I have chosen to proceed as follows. In section two I will briefly review the anatomy and physiology of the Central Nervous System (CNS). Since the workstation of the mind is apparently the CNS, it seems crucial to start with a depiction of the structure and functional mechanism of this system.

I will briefly review the scientists' present understanding of the mechanism of neurotransmission in section three.

The path of the ions through the membrane (ion) channels has always been assumed to be a straight line. Therefore, in presentation of the membrane as an electrical circuit, the channels have been displayed as simple resistors. However, in my view the path of the ions through the ion channels is helical rather than a straight line. Additionally, in section three I will try to show my proposal for a "detailed" theory of neurotransmission which regards the ion channels as inductors. One result of this theory is that the longitudinal transmission of the action potential in the nerve fibers is a wave propagation. In section four I will apply this theory to develop new definitions of thought, mind, and consciousness.

To concentrate on something means that in the brain thought is focused on one subject, and nothing else. Several parameters must be at work and in harmony to achieve this state of mind. The mechanism of concentration on a subject is discussed in section five.

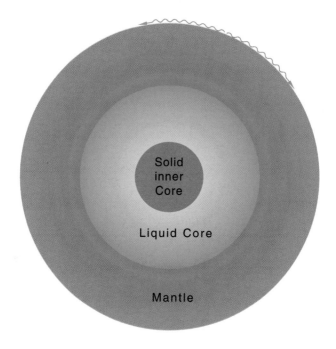

Figure 5. A schematic of the earth's layers. The crust is between 16 to 40 km. Below the crust is the mantle. The thickness of the mantle is estimated to be 2,900 km. The material of the liquid mantle is in a plastic shape due to the high pressures. At a depth of 2,900 km below the earth surface, the liquid core starts. The main element in this part is believed to be iron in its molten state. Its minimum temperature is approximately $2,000^{\circ}$C. There is some evidence that there may be a solid inner core with the radius of 1,220 km.

37 - A Brief Review of the Anatomy and Physiology of the Central Nervous System (CNS).[1,2]

The CNS is composed of the brain and the spinal cord (Fig. 1 and 2). The CNS is utilized to scan, evaluate, process, and respond to the information we receive primarily through our sense organs. Each region of the CNS is used for a certain function. These regions are as follows:[1]

1.   The spinal cord is primarily used for motor functions of skin, joints, muscles, and ligaments and conveying motor commands for movements. As figure 1 shows, the spinal cord is shorter than the vertebral column. Nevertheless, the spinal nerves extend to the end of the vertebral canal. Also these nerves extend to the outside of the canal at their level of corresponding vertebra. A spinal nerve contains *afferent* fibers, which enter the spinal cord and are specifically used to carry

information to the spinal cord and *efferent* fibers, which exit the spinal cord and are specifically used to carry information from the spinal cord to the organs. In general, the neurons themselves reside in the CNS and only their axons, dendrites, and synapses spread throughout the body. If, as a result of an injury the spinal cord is cut, then those parts of the body below the damaged point are paralyzed, i.e., lose their sensation and voluntary movement.[1]

2.   The brainstem (fig. 2a and 2b) contains the cell bodies - the nuclei of the nerve cells of the cerebellum. It is composed of three parts: first the *medulla* is the lower part, which connects the brainstem to the spinal cord. It is approximately one inch long and is used in functions such as breathing, talking, singing, swallowing, vomiting, and blood circulation. Second, (above the medulla) is the *pons* (or bridge), whose nerve cells connect to the cerebral cortex and to the cerebellum. The third part of the brainstem is the

midbrain, which is situated over the pons. The midbrain is the smallest part of the brainstem. The function of this part is the preliminary processing and subsequent leading of the audio and visual information to their appropriate centers.

The cerebellum is the control center for the motor functions. It is involved in the coordination of the range and force of movements and posture.[2]

3.   Next is the *diencephalon,* which contains the *thalamus* and *hypothalamus* (fig. 2a and 2b). The thalamus is an important switchboard for all afferent sensory input except for the sense of smell. The hypothalamus resides under the thalamus and is the center for autonomic activities. Weight balance, sexual rhythms, hunger, angers, and fatigue are among some of the functions, which are regulated and commanded through the hypothalamus.[2]

4.   Above the hypothalamus sits a reservoir of nerve centers called the *limbic system* (fig. 2) where both inborn and acquired behavior is

regulated. It also is the site of instructive behavior, motivation, and emotion including rage, fright, aggression, hunger and sexual arousal. The limbic system is connected to the hypothalamus as well as the cortical centers of the temporal lobes. Therefore, our cognitive fantasies and observations get to our conscious awareness by means of the limbic system.

5.   Finally there are the cerebral hemispheres each of which is divided by sucli or grooves into four parts: the *frontal, parietal, temporal,* and *occipital* lobes (fig. 2a). The two hemispheres are connected to each other by the *corpus callosum.* Each of the hemispheres is the center for specialized types of functions.

The frontal lobe is primarily concerned with complex motor functions including movement. The *prefrontal* fibers that reside in the forward portion of the frontal lobe are concerned with control in actions to conform to social moves.[2]

The parietal lobe is the site for the reception

of all sensory information. The primary sensory cortex is located in the parietal lobe. Within the parietal lobe an area whose size is proportional to the functional significance of the related body part represents each part of the body.

The temporal lobe is concerned with one's hearing, memory, and sense of time. Because of its connection to the limbic system, it also plays a role in our emotional experiences.

The occipital lobe is the specialized center for visual experiences. The information from the retina of the eyes is transmitted to the occipital lobe and is transformed there. Studies have shown that the two sides of the brain function in different ways. The left hemisphere works in an interpretive way seeking the logical meaning of events.[2,3] It operates in an analytic manner, breaking the received data into their most elementary constituents, then studying each element one by one. The interpretive mechanism of the left hemisphere is always at work. It always looks for order and reason, often in its own way, regardless of whether or not its interpretation of "order" and "reason" is in the appropriate context.[2] This leads the deductions of the left brain to exaggerations and thus deviations from the realistic path.

The right hemisphere of the brain, on the other hand, is concerned with the simple perceptual aspects of stimuli. Recent studies show that the use of the right brain results in a much more literal picture than that of the left brain. Therefore to observe and preserve holistic pictures of experiences and observations, the right brain works much more efficiently.[2]

On the other hand, experiments have led some psychologists to believe that every person has two types of minds, the objective and the subjective mind. Whereas the subjective mind performs only inductive reasoning, the objective mind performs both inductive and deductive reasoning. Inductive reasoning occurs when a picture of constituent elements simply is composed into a holistic conclusive picture, without further analysis of the elements. In deductive reasoning, however, the constituent elements are studied and interpreted individually, assembled conceptually and logically, and a conclusion is drawn. Therefore, in deductive reasoning a variety of conclusions may be drawn as the constituent elements are assembled in several possible ways.[3] From the previously mentioned observations of the functional mechanism of the left and right brain it is reasonable to assert that the left side of the brain is primarily influenced by the objective mind and the right brain by the subjective mind.

38 - CELLULAR NEUROPHYSIOLOGY

From neurophysiologists' observations, it has become apparent that the functions of the brain are intimately related to the number of communicating neurons as well as their interconnections. As previously mentioned, a neuron is comprised of the nucleus, a long fiber called the axon, and a varying number of branching fibers called the dendrites which extend out to the other neurons (fig. 3).[1,2]

Interneuronal information is transmitted through electrical signals flowing from the axon of one neuron to the dendrite of the second one. The contact between the two is called the synaptic contact or, simply, a synapse. The axon ending is the presynaptic membrane and the dendrite ending is the postsynaptic membrane of the synaptic contact. Although at the synapse the membranes of the two neurons are in very close contact, there is a tiny gap, the synaptic cleft, between them. An electrical impulse is transmitted across the synaptic cleft either by the induction of an electric field (the gap junction) or by release of neurotransmitters. These ions or neurotransmitters are released from the presynaptic membrane, diffused across the synaptic cleft, and are received by postsynaptic membranes.[1,4]

The specific and precise connections of neurons with certain other neurons are what are considered to be responsible for the functional mechanisms of the CNS. There are about 10^{15} synapses in the human brain. Whereas some of these synaptic contacts are between two neighboring neurons, there are some neurons with long axons, which make synaptic contacts meters away. A single neuron can also make numerous contacts.[2,4]

As I mentioned before, neural electrical signals, either inductive or transmitted by ions, are the heralds of the CNS. Therefore, every new thought process is handled by a new set of synaptic connections. In fact, memory itself is a set of synaptic connections engraved in the network of neurons. This paradigm paraphrases the functional mechanism of the mind utilizing the CNS, insomuch as the synaptic contacts are the mind's emissaries for either or both perception and conveyance of the inner and outer world. Thus to discern the principles and mechanisms of neural signaling is of primary importance in our ultimate quest to grasp who we are and what we are.[2]

Let us now look at the mechanism by which a neuron responds to a stimulus and the propagation of the effect of that stimulus along the nerve fiber. Generally speaking, a nerve cell responds to a stimulus by changing the electrical properties of its cell membrane. In its unexcited state, an electric potential difference exists across the membrane of a living cell. This so-called resting membrane potential amounts to 50-100 mV, with the cell interior being of lower potential.[1]

This potential difference is due to an imbalance of concentrated ions between the inner and outer parts of the cell membrane. The main ions to participate in producing the membrane potential difference are Na^+, K^+, Cl^-, and Ca^{2+}. Only the nerve and muscle cells show excitability; which means the cells respond to a stimulus by producing transient changes in the ion conductances thus, the electric potential difference of their membranes. Basically, in a nerve cell, stimuli increase the positive ion concentration of the outer membrane and thereby increase the magnitude of the potential difference. This is called depolarization. When the potential difference reaches a critical value, i.e., the threshold, the Na^+ channel (pathways through which the Na^+ ions penetrate inside the cell) open. This results in an abrupt, enormous increase in the Na^+ membrane conductance (or decrease in its resistance), hence a fast Na^+ flux into the cell. As a result of this, the negative potential of the inside of the cell is reduced in magnitude, i.e. the potential difference approaches zero. The critical value of the potential difference at which the Na^+ channels are activated is called the action potential. Therefore, the effect of the stimuli on the neuron is the production of an action potential. Apparently the action potential propagates along the neuronal fiber. It then reaches the synapses where it either stimulates the release of the neurotransmitters or induces an electric field on the postsynaptic membrane across the synaptic cleft. The propagation of the action potential across the nerve fiber does not seem to occur as it does in electrical wires. Both the large value of the longitudinal electrical resistance of the nerve fiber and the weakness of its insulation prevent a cable-like transmission along the nerve fiber.[1,4]

What neurophysiologists believe happens, is that after the local action potential causes the local Na^+ channels to open, the inside of the membrane becomes, locally, more positively charged. This

difference in the charge density between the
neighboring sections along the fiber results in the
charge moving longitudinally both in the inside
and the outside of the cell membrane. This
longitudinal shift of the electrons is the equivalent
of the longitudinal shift of the action potential.[1,4]

Nevertheless, since the electrical properties
of the excitable cells are very similar to those of
electrical circuits, usually in electrophysiology,
the membrane is demonstrated by electrical
circuits. In linear cable theory the nerve fiber is
assumed to have constant electrical resistance,
both longitudinal and transverse. However, first I
will review the approach of the nonlinear theory,
which resembles the linear case and also is a more
general approach.[4]

Hodjkin and Hoxley proposed a model of the
circuitry of the cell membrane (of the squid
axon).[4-7] First, they used the parallel conductance
model to describe the major ionic conductances in
the squid axon (fig. 4).[4] In figure 4: g_K, g_{Na}, and

g_L are the conductances (the inverse of the electrical resistance R). The parameters ε_K, ε_{Na}, and ε_L are the potentials when the cell is at rest. The currents I_K, I_{Na}, and I_L are those of K^+, Na^+, and L, the escaping ions, respectively. Here, the conductances are assumed to be functions of both the applied electric potential and time. Having a negatively charged inner surface and a positively charged outer surface, the membrane of the cell acts like a capacitor, shown by C_m, in the circuit. Here, C_m is the membrane capacitance of a strip of the cylinder of the fiber with an area of 1 cm^2. From fig. 4 it is clear that the membrane current I_m, is equal to the sum of all of the currents, i.e.

$$I_m = I_C + I_K + I_{Na} + I_L, \qquad (1)$$

where $I_C = dQ/dt = C_m (dV/dt)$, therefore

$$I_m = C_m (dV/dt) + I_K + I_{Na} + I_L. \qquad (2)$$

Assuming the resistors obey Ohm's law, one can write

$$I_m = C_m \, (dV/dt) + (V - \varepsilon_K)g_K + (V - \varepsilon_{Na}) \, g_{Na} + (V - \varepsilon_L)g_L. \tag{3}$$

Hodjkin and Hoxley suggested that the K^+ and Na^+ conductances are the products of the probability of the gates being open, Y_K (V,t) and Y_{Na} (V,t), and maximum conductances, $\widetilde{g}_K$ and $\widetilde{g}_{Na}$, respectively. Here $0 \leq (Y_K$ and $Y_{Na}) \leq 1$ are called the gating variables. Using the experimental data, Hodjkin and Hoxley proposed their solutions to the gating variables and thus to the voltage and time variations of conductances.[4-7]

Hodjkin and Hoxley later presented their model of the propagation of the action potential along the axon. Figure 5 shows the equivalent circuit of a cable for a part of an axon. Here

$V_m(x,t)$ is the potential difference between the inside and the outside of the membrane and c_m is the capacitance per unit length of the cable. Employing Ohm's law, we conclude the longitudinal drop in the membrane potential is equal to the product of the internal resistance and current. One can write

$$\partial V_m (x, t)/\partial x = - r_i i_i. \qquad (4)$$

Here, r_i is the axial resistance per unit length of the axon's cross-section and i_i is the internal current. Some of i_i though, escape out of the membrane through r_m and c_m. Therefore,

$$\partial i_i /\partial x = -i_m \qquad (5)$$

Combining these two equations

$$i_m = r_i^{-1} \frac{\partial^2 V_m}{\partial x^2} , \qquad (6)$$

Appendix **I** shows that $c_m = 2\pi a\, C_m$, $r_m = 2\pi a\, R_m$, r_i $= \pi a^2 R_i$ with R_i being the resistivity of the axon, and $i_m = 2\pi a\, I_m$. Using these relations and that

$$i_m = r_i^{-1}\,\frac{\partial\, V_m}{\partial\, t} + I_K + I_{Na} + I_L\ , \text{ we have}$$

$$a/2R_i = \frac{\partial^2 V_m}{\partial\, x^2} = c_m\,\frac{\partial\, V_m}{\partial\, t} \quad + I_K + I_{Na} + I_L, \ (7)$$

At this point most neurophysiologists reason that because the propagation speed of the action potential is almost constant, then:[5]

$$V\,(x,\, t) = f\,(x - \theta\, t), \tag{8}$$

where θ is the propagation speed. Therefore the partial derivatives of V are related to each other as follows:

and $$\frac{\partial\, V_m}{\partial\, x} = \frac{-1}{\theta}\,\frac{\partial\, V_m}{\partial\, t} \tag{9}$$

$$\frac{\partial^2 V_m}{\partial\, x^2} = \frac{1}{\theta^2}\,\frac{\partial^2 V_m}{\partial\, t^2} \tag{10}$$

Equation (10) is that of the propagation of a wave. Thus using the constancy of the propagation speed, Hodjkin and Hoxley inferred that the propagation of the action potential must be wavelike. No further explanation appears in the neurophysiology literature.[4-6] Using Eq. (10) we can rewrite Eq. (7) as

$$\frac{a}{2\,R_i\,\theta^2}\,\frac{\partial^2\,V_m}{\partial\,t^2} = c_m\frac{\partial\,V_m}{\partial\,t} + I_K + I_{Na} + I_L \qquad (11)$$

Reference 5 expresses *"...the major disadvantage [of Eq. (11)] is that the value of θ is required in advance in order to solve this equation. ... by a process of successive approximation the correct value of θ may be obtained to an arbitrary degree of accuracy."*

Hodjkin and Hoxley's predicted θ was quite close to the experimental value.[5] Their estimated value of the propagation speed of the action potential is $\theta \approx 18.8$ m/s.[4]

One major point not considered by any theory of the propagation of action potential is that the path of the ions through the ion channels may not be a straight line. [4-7] Figure 6 shows the sliding helix (the S4 sub-unit) model of voltage-gated Na^+ channel. [4] This model propounds that the S4 helices respond to membrane depolarization by rotating 60° while moving outward by about 5A°. Since the positively charged amino acid residues in S4 are separated by about 5A° from one another, the above rotation produces charge displacement analogous to moving one charge across the whole membrane. [4] Actually, the path of the ions themselves is, perhaps, helical, as shown in the studies of ionophores. [8] Ionophores are molecules which exceedingly expand the membrane's permeability to cations such as K^+, Na^+, and H^+. Some ionophores are channel formers and some are ion carriers. Gramicidin is an example of channel forming ionophores. This antibiotic is a polypeptide with 15 amino acids. When inserted into a membrane, the gramicidin polypeptide assumes a helical shape. Accordingly, the actual path of the ions through these molecules is helical.[8]

This helicity of the ion path changes the membrane circuit substantially since inductors representing the helical movement of the ions must be added.

Figure 7 shows the "corrected" electric circuit of the membrane. Here, I have added the inductors as an indication of the fact that the motion of ions through their channels (as well as that of the channel gates) is spiral. Here, I_K, I_{Na}, and I_L, R_K, R_{Na}, and R_L, L_K, L_{Na}, and L_L, ε_K, ε_{Na}, and ε_L represent the electric current, resistance, inductance, and resting potentials of K^+, N^+, and other ions, respectively. C_m Symbolizes the capacitor behavior of the membrane. For that part of the neuron fiber affected by the action potential, V_0, the initial membrane potential is the same as V_m only at t = 0, while the initial current is zero. Using Kirchhoff's current and voltage laws[9] for the three loops, each containing the capacitor and one of the ion group resistance, inductance, and resting potential, we have

$$\mathcal{E}_K - R_K I_K - L_K \frac{d\,I_K}{d\,t} + \frac{Q_m}{C_m} = 0 \qquad (12)$$

$$-\mathcal{E}_{Na} - R_{Na} I_{Na} - L_{Na} \frac{d\,I_{Na}}{d\,t} + \frac{Q_m}{C_m} = 0 \qquad (13)$$

$$\mathcal{E}_L - R_L I_L - L_L \frac{d\,I_L}{d\,t} + \frac{Q_m}{C_m} = 0 \qquad (14)$$

Dividing each equation by its pertinent L, adding them, defining

$$\frac{1}{L} \equiv \frac{1}{L_K} + \frac{1}{L_{Na}} + \frac{1}{L_L}, \qquad (15)$$

$$\frac{\mathcal{E}_\lambda}{L} \equiv \frac{\mathcal{E}_K}{L_K} - \frac{\mathcal{E}_{Na}}{L_{Na}} + \frac{\mathcal{E}_L}{L_L}, \qquad (16)$$

and assuming the ratio of resistance, R, to inductance, L, to be the same for all channels and

defining γ as

$$\gamma \equiv \frac{R}{L} \equiv \frac{R_K}{L_K} = \frac{R_{Na}}{L_{Na}} = \frac{R_L}{L_L} \quad , \qquad (17)$$

The following equation is concluded

$$\frac{\varepsilon_\lambda}{L} - \gamma\left(I_K + I_{Na} + I_L\right) -$$

$$\frac{d}{dt}\left(I_K + I_{Na} + I_L\right) + \frac{Q_m}{LC_m} = 0. \qquad (18)$$

Using

$I_K + I_{Na} + I_L = I_m - I_c$, we have

$$\frac{\varepsilon_\lambda}{L} - \gamma(I_m - I_c) - \frac{d}{dt}(I_m - I_c) + \frac{Q_m}{LC_m} = 0 \qquad (19)$$

Equation (19) is exactly the same as that for a circuit embodying a battery of potential, ε_λ, an inductor L, a resistor R, and a capacitor Cm, connected in series. Therefore, the membrane circuit of three ion channels is equivalent to a circuit of one ion channel of figure 8. Taking the time derivative of Eq. (19) while assuming the terms γ and L and $\dfrac{\varepsilon_\lambda}{L}$ to be constants (the linear case), we have

$$-\gamma\ \frac{d}{dt}\left(I_m - I_c\right)\ -\ \frac{d^2}{dt^2}\left(I_m - I_c\right)\ +\ \frac{I_c}{LC_m} \qquad (20)$$

which can be rearranged to yield

$$\frac{d^2 I_m}{dt^2} + \gamma\frac{d\,I_m}{dt} - \frac{d^2 I_c}{dt^2} - \gamma\,\frac{d\,I_c}{dt} - \frac{I_c}{LC_m} = 0 \qquad (21)$$

Note that $\dfrac{d\,Q_m}{dt} = I_c$ (fig. 7). Since Eq. (21) must hold true, one way to solve it is to assume the first two terms (i.e. the terms which contain I_m) to be identically equal to zero. Then we have

$$\frac{d^2 I_m}{dt^2} + \gamma\frac{d\,I_m}{dt} = 0 \qquad (22)$$

and

$$\frac{d^2 I_c}{dt^2} + \gamma\,\frac{d\,I_c}{dt} + \frac{I_c}{LC_m} = 0 \qquad (23)$$

Solving Eq. (22), we find

$$I_m = I_0 \, e^{-\gamma t} , \qquad (24)$$

where I_m (t = 0) = I_0 , while noting that the initial potential, V_0 , produces an initial I_m and that I_m(t → ∞) = 0. After t = γ^{-1} sec., I_m = $0.37 I_0$ and after t=$4\gamma^{-1}$ sec., I_m = $0.0\,2\,I_0$.

Moving ahead to solve Eq. (23), we take I_c = A e^{xt} , which results in

$$x^2 + \gamma x + \frac{1}{LC_m} = 0. \qquad (25)$$

Solving this quadratic equation for x, we have

$$X = \frac{-1}{2} \gamma \pm \frac{1}{2} \left[\gamma^2 - \frac{4}{LC_m} \right]^{1/2} \qquad (26)$$

For $\gamma^2 \geq \frac{4}{LC_m}$, we acquire x < 0. Thus, I_C will be

equal to the exponential of a negative number for all times. This means I_C (t → ∞) = 0. On the other hand for $\gamma^2 < \dfrac{4}{LC_m}$ we have

$$I_C = A\, e^{-\gamma t/2}\, e^{\pm i\,\Delta\, t/2},\qquad(27)$$

where $\Delta = \left[\dfrac{4}{LC_m} - \gamma^2\right]^{1/2} > 0$, and $i = \sqrt{-1}$.

Equation (27) indicates that in general the current across the two sides of the membrane, or the equivalent inductor of the ion channels L, is a damped oscillatory function of time. Obviously the damping time depends on γ or the ratio of resistance to the self-inductance of the ion channels. Since the real part of the function in Eq. (27) is our answer to I_C, then we have

$$I_C = A\, e^{-\gamma t/2}\, \sin\!\left(\tfrac{\Delta}{2}t\right)\qquad(28)$$

Considering that

$$V_m(t) = Cm \int_0^t I_c\,(t)dt , \text{ and that}$$

$V_m(0) = V_0$, we can demonstrate

$$V_m(t) = V_0 \, e^{-\gamma t/2} \left[\cos \left(\frac{\Delta}{2} t \right) + \frac{\gamma}{\Delta} \sin \left(\frac{\Delta}{2} t \right) \right]$$

(29)

and

$$A = - C_m V_0 \frac{\Delta}{2} \left(1 + \frac{\gamma^2}{\Delta^2} \right)$$

(30)

which results in

$$I_C = C_m V_0 \frac{\Delta}{2} \left(1 + \frac{\gamma^2}{\Delta^2} \right) e^{-\gamma t/2} \mathrm{Sin} \left(\frac{\Delta}{2} t \right)$$

(31)

Hence the current of the inductor,

$$I_\lambda = I_K + I_{Na} + I_L = I_m - I_c \; , \; \text{is}$$

$$I_\lambda(t) = I_0 \, e^{-\gamma t} - C_m V_0 \frac{\Delta}{2} \left(1 + \frac{\gamma^2}{\Delta^2} \right) e^{-\gamma t/2} \mathrm{Sin} \left(\frac{\Delta}{2} t \right)$$

(32)

Equation (32) shows that the ionic current of the equivalent channel, due to the action potential, is a damping oscillatory function of time. However according to Faraday's law of induction,[9] before damping this time varying current induces currents in neighboring ion channels (inductors), yielding in the inductive propagation of the potential.

An intriguing aspect of this model emerges when we investigate the propagation of the capacitative, or the inductive, current-potential along the nerve fiber. Since all of the circuits resemble each other, all can be replaced with their equivalent circuits containing only one inductor L. Essentially according to Faraday's law of induction,[9] the variable magnetic field of the first inductor induces an electromotive force, EMF, across its neighboring inductor, $L_2 = L$. In general the induced EMF, by any inductor, L_1, on another inductor, L_2, is given by

$$E \, M \, F = -M_{12} \frac{d \, I_1}{d \, t} \tag{33}$$

where $I_1 = I_1$ (t) in the present case. The coefficient M_{12} is the mutual inductance and in general is given by [9]

$$M_{12} = \sqrt{L_1 L_2} \qquad (34)$$

In the present case, since $L_1 = L_2 = L$, we have

$$M_{12} = L. \qquad (35)$$

Thus, the induced $E M F_2$ in the inductor adjacent to the one acted on by the action potential, V_0, is

$$EMF_2 = -L \frac{d I_\lambda}{d t} \qquad (36)$$

This EMF_2 produces a current in the second inductor, which can be found through

$$-L_2 \frac{d I_2}{d t} = -L \frac{d I_2}{d t} = E M F_2 \qquad (37)$$

From Eqs. (36) and (37) it is unequivocal that $I_2 = I_\lambda$, Consequently, the induced current in the second inductor adjacent to the first one, is exactly the same as the current of the first inductor – with the same damping oscillatory functions of time. Again, before complete damping the secondary current induces a tertiary current in its neighboring inductor. Similarly, the tertiary and all of the other subsequent induced currents are precisely the same as $I_1(t)$ of Eq. (32). In an identical manner the induction of EMF continues all the way across the nerve fiber. Consequently, the effect of the action potential is communicated among the channels of the membrane resulting in the longitudinal motion of the potential. Due to the electrical resistively of the channels, however, in each circuit, part of the energy of the induced EMF - the induced potential - converts to heat, resulting in a gradual reduction in the magnitude of the longitudinally moving potential.

A point about my suggested circuits of the membrane ion channels is the fact that each of these capacitor-inductor circuits performs as a radio receiver and transmitter. Thus, the joined performance of these circuits is also that of a radio transmitter and receiver. I will elaborate on this later.

An offshoot of this model is that when the

electrical resistance of every ion channel is zero, i.e., the channels are superconducting. This brings about the subject of room-temperature (T~300k) superconductivity. In Appendix III I have extensively discussed my (new) theory of superconductivity. There I discussed both the conventional and the so called high Tc superconductors. Based on this novel theory I suggest the type of material which would be a superconductor at room temperature.

This insinuates $\gamma = 0$ and the circuit reduces to parallel inductors that are in parallel with the capacitors of the membrane. Equation (12), (13) and (14), which were found using Kirchhoff's laws, reduce to the following equations

$$\varepsilon_K - L_K \frac{d\,I_K}{d\,t} + \frac{Q_m}{C_m} = 0, \tag{38}$$

$$-\varepsilon_{Na} - L_{Na} \frac{d\,I_{Na}}{d\,t} + \frac{Q_m}{C_m} = 0, \tag{39}$$

$$\varepsilon_L - L_L \frac{d\,I_L}{d\,t} + \frac{Q_m}{C_m} = 0. \tag{40}$$

Again, dividing Eq. (38), (39), and (40) by L_K, L_{Na}, and L_L respectively, and then adding them together we have

$$\frac{\varepsilon_\lambda}{L} - \frac{d}{dt}\left(I_K + I_{Na} + I_L\right) + \frac{1}{L}\frac{Q_m}{C_m} = 0, \quad (41)$$

where again $\frac{1}{L} \equiv \frac{1}{L_K} + \frac{1}{L_{Na}} + \frac{1}{L_L}$ and $\frac{\varepsilon_\lambda}{L}$.

$\equiv \frac{\varepsilon_K}{L_K} - \frac{\varepsilon_{Na}}{L_{Na}} + \frac{\varepsilon_L}{L_L}$ Equation (41) is that for a circuit containing one inductor of self-inductance L, a battery of potential ε_λ, and a capacitor C_m (fig.9).   Therefore, we can conceive of the capacitor of membrane C_m, embodying single ion channel L, with a resting potential ε_λ.   The substituted form of Eq. (41) is

$$\frac{\varepsilon_\lambda}{L} - \frac{dI_\lambda}{dt} + \frac{Q_m}{LC_m} = 0, \quad (42)$$

with I_λ $(=I_K + I_{Na} + I_L = I_m - I_C)$ the equivalent current through the inductor L. Taking the time derivative of Eq. (42) and assuming L to be

constant, we have

$$\frac{d^2 I_c}{d t^2} + \frac{I_c}{L C_m} - \frac{d^2 I_m}{d t^2} = 0 \tag{43}$$

Again $\frac{d Q_m}{d t} = I_c$. One solution to the above equation is when the terms including I_c are equal to zero, concurring to which we have

$$\frac{d^2 I_m}{d t^2} = 0, \tag{44}$$

and

$$\frac{d^2 I_c}{d t^2} + \frac{I_c}{LC_m} = 0 \tag{45}$$

The solution to Eq. (44) is $I_m = A t + B$. Nevertheless, both A and B must be identically equal to zero because otherwise the current becomes infinitely large or persists forever respectively, thus $I_m = 0$. The solution to Eq. (45) is

$$I_c = -V_0 \, \omega \, C_m \, \sin \omega \, t, \tag{46}$$

where again $\omega = \sqrt{\frac{1}{LC_m}}$. The coefficient $-V_0 \, \omega C_m$ in Eq. (46) is found regarding the initial condition $V_m(0) = V_0$. Also with $I_m = 0$, we have

$$I_\lambda = -I_C = V_0 \, \omega \, C_m \, \sin \omega \, t. \tag{47}$$

Equation (47) asserts that the current in the inductor, as well as that in the capacitor, is an oscillatory function of time, persisting forever while its magnitude never surpasses $V_0 \omega \, C_m$. It can be shown that the potential across the inductor and the capacitor is

$$V_\lambda = -V_C = V_0 \, \cos \omega \, t, \tag{48}$$

which also is an enduring oscillatory function of time.

with $\dfrac{c^2}{\mu \varepsilon} = v^2$. The general solution to Eq. (50)

is

$$\vec{B} = \vec{B}_0 \sin (\omega t + k x), \tag{51}$$

where $k v = \omega$. From Eq. (51) it is clear that in its movement from one inductor to the other the magnetic field $\vec{B}$ gains a phase. $\Delta\phi = k x_0$.

According to Eq. (51), the propagation speed of the action potential in the nerve fiber is $v = \dfrac{c}{\sqrt{\mu \varepsilon}}$. This is unquestionably much greater than the speed with which the information from different parts of the body reaches the brain ($v \approx$ 20 m/s).[4] I believe the propagation of the action potential is slowed down at the synapses by the process of presynaptic release of neurotransmitters, their motion across the synaptic cleft, and the postsynaptic stimulation of the dendrites. Therefore, the observed speed of $v \approx 20$ m/s is the collective average of the longitudinal speed of the action potential along the nerve fibers.

The frequency of the neurotransmitters' release is also the same as that of the action potential in the ion channel inductors. Hence, the postsynaptic fibers also oscillate with the same frequency as that of the presynaptic fiber. This indicates that all nerve fibers between the point of stimulation and the data processing center in the brain oscillate with the same frequency.

As mentioned, the single circuit (including the membrane capacitor, the ion channel, inductors and resistors) acts as a radio receiver and transmitter. Consequently, the nerve fibers, the neurons, and the whole CNS are radio receivers and transmitters. In the next sections I will use this remarkable discovery to redefine the mind, thinking, concentration, the mechanism of our mental functions and other related phenomena.

39 - THE MIND

The quest for what is mind is one of the oldest problems known to mankind. In the course of history there have been numerous philosophical attempts to answer this question. Science too, has begun to provide a solution to this problem.[10] Scientists have generally agreed that there is no "mind" separate and distinct from the brain.[2] Therefore, to understand the "mind," most scientists believe we should understand the structures and functions of the brain. Certainly the CNS is the agent through which the mind communicates with the material world. However, it is my contention that the mind cannot be understood by increasingly careful studies of the CNS. This is as nonsensical as attempting to understand E&M waves by carefully studying different elements of radios and TV's.

In the last section I demonstrated that the way our CNS communicates with any entity is through a series of electromagnetic (E&M) oscillations. In fact, I postulated that the CNS is like a radio receiver and transmitter, which is connected to the world by E&M waves. On this basis, I hypothesize that the brain is like a radio and the mind is similar to radio waves propagating in time and space throughout the universe. One type of thinking occurs when the brain is tuned in to receive and transmit within certain bands of frequencies.

In the previous section I showed that in general there are two types of waves carried through the nerve fibers: The first waves which are of short duration. I relate these short-lived waves to our instant and short-term memories. The attenuation of this type of signal is determined by the value of $\gamma \left(\equiv \dfrac{R}{L} = \dfrac{R_K}{L_K} = \dfrac{R_{Na}}{L_{Na}} = \dfrac{R_L}{L_L} \right)$. Therefore, the less resistive the ion channels are the longer the signals' duration. The second type of waves are those signals for which $\gamma \equiv 0$. In essence, when the ion channels have no electrical resistance, or in the perpendicular direction the membrane is superconducting, the signals last forever. I relate these long lived waves to our long-term memories. Through the synaptic connections, the net inductance and capacitance of a center in our brain can be, and is, changed. This makes it possible for the brain to be tuned in to a certain band of frequencies. I identify this process with thinking. Primarily, inductive thinking transpires when the brain receives a certain band of frequencies and perception occurs without further manipulation or processing. On the other hand, deductive thinking transpires when the brain both receives and processes the E&M waves.

The processing of the waves received by the brain is only possible by means of interference. Thus, it is feasible to state that all of our reactions arise from the interference of arriving waves with those already existing in their respective centers. The phenomenon of interference is an intriguing one. Through Fourier analysis, one can show fundamentally any number of waves interfere and consummate to a periodic function. Conversely, every periodic function can be expressed as a combination of a series of harmonics. One can write[9]

$$f(x,t) = \sum_{n=1}^{m} A_n \sin(\omega_n t + k_n x) + B_n \cos(\omega_n t + k_n x), \tag{52}$$

$f(x+L, t+T) = f(x,t)$ and m is a natural number.

Accordingly, through interference, the arriving waves combine with the old ones and thereupon give rise to a responsive resultant. The conscious mind is the collective file of already existing waves and their interferences. Conversely, the unconscious mind could be those waves which have not yet arrived at our system. However, as I will discuss, by means of mental concentration our system is able to receive and process the related new waves and make them conscious.

New E&M waves can arrive either through

our five senses or directly by tuning the respective brain processing centers on the waves. Those waves, which are within reach of one or a combination of our five senses and stimulate the nerve fibers to the threshold level of the action potential, become part of the conscious mind.

On the other hand, imagine an event transpiring at spatial-temporal coordinates out of reach of the observer's five senses or an event emitting waves weaker than the threshold level of our sensibility. This event cannot be sensed by the conscious mind. Nevertheless considering that any event radiates its characteristic E&M waves, once the conscious mind is tuned into the same wavelengths, it is able to receive the event. Depending on whether the brain is noise free and concurrently can amplify the signals (to the level of threshold action potential), the signal is sensed. In essence, the brain is just like any other E&M receiver whose reception can be enhanced by the rectification and amplification of the incoming signals. Yet what is a rectifier-amplifier brain?

A counterpart of a noise free brain is one, which is both physically and mentally healthy and balanced. In previous chapters, I have discussed the profound importance of deep breathing in the maintenance and enhancement of cold fusion in the entire body. As I mentioned before, a deep inspiration results in a tenfold increase in the amount of the O_2 intake by the blood. The circulation of this O_2 rich blood and its deliverance to the mitochondria results in as much as a tenfold consumption of carbohydrates thus a tenfold production of H^+ ions. This will enhance the number of cold fusions taking place in the entire body. The extra energy produced by the auxiliary number of cold fusions is exploited in an increased production of B&T cells, which are responsible for the sanitation of the body (including the CNS). A healthy and unpolluted CNS is better balanced to do its job without noise interferences. This will partially compensate for what I call a noise free CNS (a radio receiver of the E&M waves).

As I previously mentioned, another determining factor in aiding the CNS to sense the out-of-reach or weak signals is the amplification of the signal. This introduces us to the thesis of concentration, which will be discussed in section 40.

40 · CONCENTRATION

Close attention, convergence, collection, compaction, and consolidation -- these are some synonyms for the word concentration. All of these concepts are concerned with the act of gathering distinct and separate constituents as closely to each other as possible. This is exactly what our goal should be when we concentrate on a subject or an object. In order to concentrate on a matter beyond the present reach of our five senses perhaps the first thing we do is to recall the strongest memories we have of that matter. This collection of past experiences in the form of memory is accompanied by (at least a partial) dismissal of other thoughts.

Thinking, at its lower level, is basically the localized interferences or interactions of the existing waves in the brain. At a more profound level, thinking can be defined as the interference of the broadcasted E&M waves of the brain with

All of the induced EMFs would actually be in phase had the position of all of the ion channel inductors been the same. Nevertheless, in one-dimensional cases, the inductors are positioned alongside one another necessitating a traveling of the electromagnetic field from one inductor to the other along the x-axis. Using Maxwell's equations, it can easily be shown that the spatial-temporal variation of the magnetic field itself is wavelike. The wave equation for the propagation of the electromagnetic field in three-dimensional space with permittivity ε and permeability μ is

$$\nabla^2 \vec{B} = \frac{\mu \varepsilon}{c^2} \frac{\partial^2 \vec{B}}{\partial t^2} \tag{49}$$

In one dimension this equation reduces to

$$\frac{\partial^2 \vec{B}}{\partial x^2} = \frac{\mu \varepsilon}{c^2} \frac{\partial^2 \vec{B}}{\partial t^2}, \tag{50}$$

those existing in the universe. This type of thinking, I term as "deep thinking" and it is mainly accomplished, I feel, by scholars. Pioneers of knowledge do the deepest type of thinking, I feel. These pioneers immerse themselves in completely "new" waves propagating in the universe without bringing any of their own preexisting waves. My father and teacher Professor Sadegh Angha describes this type of thought as being "like a mirror whose attribute is to cease to manifest."

In order to accomplish more profound levels of thinking one needs to delve more deeply into the E&M waves (images) of the subject and temporarily dismiss other waves. This dismissal of unrelated waves and subsequent immersion in those relevant to the subject I term concentration. Concentration is, therefore, the amplification of the waves of a subject in conjunction with the fine-tuning of the radio receiver (i.e., the brain) into the waves transmitted by the subject. Moreover, this dismissal or avoidance of other waves

corresponds to the other stages of rectification,
i.e., freeing the system of noise.

The degree of being finely tuned into the
waves of a particular subject is representative of
the level of concentration. Perhaps the most
conspicuous   physiological   indicator   of
concentration is that of the increased electrical
activity of the neurons related to the waves of the
subject. This increase in the amplitude of the
electrical current culminates in a more acidic
environment in the relevant neurons and a
correspondingly higher number of H^+ ions there.
This increase in the H^+ ion population results in an
enhancement of cold fusion, and consequently, the
energy production of the relevant neurons. This
could be likened to a house (the brain) with many
rooms (neuron centers) whose lights are suddenly
and simultaneously brightened. The extra energy
of these neurons is spent on the amplification of
the existing specific signals. Due to the fact that
the neurons are transmitters as well as receivers,

both the transmission and reception power of these specific signals is intensified. This amplification of the special selected signal diminishes the presence of other waves. Thus, the brain is more closely attuned into trading those signified waves.

In summary, the increase in the electrical current results in an increase in the rate of cold fusion. This amplifies the energy production (in the neurons) which in turn results in the amplification of their oscillations. The combination of concentration and deep breathing result in an even higher rate of cold fusion in the relevant neurons. The brain's amplification of the selected signals thereby also increases.

The high rate of fusion resulting from a combination of deep breathing and concentration can occur in any body organ. When we concentrate on a body organ, the nerve fibers in that organ undergo greater electrification producing a larger number of localized fusions. Furthermore, deep breathing raises the level of fusion throughout the body including that organ. The ultimate outcome of these processes is a greater energy production; the rate of which is dependent both on the degree of concentration as well as the method of breathing. Some consequences of the production of this auxiliary energy include the attainment of reconstruction as needed in the organ (thus, the maintenance of the organ's health) and the enhancement of the functionality of the organ and the rate of E&M radiation from the organ. This is the incentive behind the breathing and concentration methods in yoga as well as other disciplines.

Included in the spectrum of E&M radiation are the infrared or, loosely called, heat waves. Thus, the E&M waves radiated from the organs of the body contain the infrared or the thermal part of the spectrum. On the other hand, generally the number and the distribution of the nerve fibers or the nerves themselves in a specific organ is a characteristic of the organ itself. Therefore, the rate of fusion and consequently the radiation of thermal energy from an organ are illustrative of the organ. I will present an extensive essay on this subject in the future.

Although approaches may vary with disciplines, all disciplines begin with deep breathing accompanied by repose. Commonly the environment is quiet, comfortable, exotically and/or naturally beautiful, and scented. It may be noiseless or furnished with soft melodies or natural sounds such as birds singing, the wind blowing, sea water smashing into the shore, or water running through the river bed. These environmental preparations are aimed at attracting the apprentice's attention to designated environmental objects (thus nourishing the relevant E&M waves in the brain) and reducing the numerous and disorganized interference's of fruitless E&M waves.

The next phase in the attainment of concentration is to focus the student's attention on his/her own body thus intensifying those E&M waves pertaining to the body. While the deep breathing continues, the student is instructed to assume different postures. In some disciplines the student is supposed to sit motionless for a long time without any movement. The purpose of postures, however, is to focus the student's attention (i.e., energize the associated E&M waves of his /her memory) on the relevant body part by stimulating the relevant nerves. At this stage, in some disciplines the student is asked to visualize the anatomy of the intended part(s). This further energizes the desired E&M waves. It should be mentioned, however, that even partial execution of the postures is usually accompanied by the experience of some pain by beginners. Nevertheless, it is exactly this pain which continuously nourishes the interferences of the suitable waves. In order to accomplish the posture, the student exerts pressure on a part of his/her body. These stress forces stimulate the nerve fibers generating the action potential, which is conducted to the brain increasing the related interferences. Endurance at this stage acquires and/or maintains the student's physical and mental health, plus disciplines the student to avoid the unintended abortive interferences of the E&M waves in his (her) brain.

At this level the student is ready to begin what is mistakenly called "meditation." What is usually intended by "meditation" are, in fact, higher levels of concentration. The student is instructed to sit in a preferably dark room and look at one thing, such as candlelight or a dot on the wall. Ideally, he/she is not permitted to think about anything, but just observes. Practically no interference of waves, other than those needed for his basic vital activities, is allowed to take place in his/her brain. Upon the realization of observation without interference, the antenna of the student's radio-TV, i.e., the brain, is open to receive the new (to him/her) waves about the observed object. After reception, the whole system is now ready to amplify and project the waves to the related centers. This state is much like a healthy baby's while looking at an alien object.

In some disciplines, the student sits in a dark room and, while closing his eyes, visualizes one thing or thinks about one subject. The unity of the subject is of primary importance, in light of the fact that the student's brain should be finely tuned into and amplify only one band of frequencies. This is the level where the individual's broadcasted waves are so vigorously connected to the radio (the brain) itself that any interference and resulting disturbance is relayed back to the radio (the brain) and is recognized.

Every scientific discovery takes place in this manner. The scientist enthusiastically researches a problem. After a continuance of time, the central point of the puzzle appears. Since this perplexing point cannot be resolved with conventional understandings, he/she is compelled to pause and repeatedly and continuously review the problem. The immersion into the problem becomes so deep it is as if there is only one living thing in his/her mind. Indeed, this must occur before the discovery can take place. Seemingly, in the shortest time span, the scientist's most sharply and finely tuned radio transmitter (brain) amplifies the waves of the problem (floating in space) to a perceptible level. Like a radio, the receiver (brain) senses the waves with its antenna,[11] sends them to the proper neurons which are specified to vibrate with those frequencies of the problem, these neurons amplify the waves, and finally communicate the waves with other parts of the brain to process the data. Consequently, the solution finds its place within the context of the scientist's structure of knowledge.

The final step of the student's ascent upward on the "concentration ladder" is his /her total submission to a special band of wavelengths. However, like all stages, which are continuations of the last lower planes, this too is a continuum of the previous one. Very rarely does one encounter a discipline with rules and trainings to achieve this level. The student must disengage a substantial number of impurities which are not only energy consuming, but also upset the delicate tuning necessary. At this level the student's radio-TV reception is perfected, i.e., there is no noise. Virtually, here the student is continuously in the reception or the discovery state. It is this perpetuity which differentiates this level from the last one. He/she is entirely submitted to the waves as if he/she is annihilated in the waves, identically like a radio or TV. (Whereas a scientist's receiver has separate concurrence with the waves of a problem, a student of this level is always in reception of new waves). This is a level where the consciousness of the student centralizes in the broadcasted waves so thoroughly that he/she becomes one with the waves.

Huygens' principle maintains that E&M

waves propagate on temporally expanding spheres while every point on their front becomes a new source of radiation. On the other hand, according to Einstein's equation of time dilation,

$$\Delta t' = \Delta t \Big/ \left(1 - \frac{v^2}{c^2} \right)^{1/2}$$

where c is the speed of light, v is the relative speed of two frames, and Δt and $\Delta t'$ are the time intervals measured in the moving and stationary frame of references, respectively. Therefore, from the standpoint of an E&M wave (which itself is light), time freezes. Consequently in our standpoint, during "no" conceivable time the apprentice's consciousness journeys deep into the universe. In Sufism this level is called "The Journey of Horizons" where enormous new horizons of thought are attained in "no" time. This is the path to consciously become aware of the universe.

However, the human brain, just like a radio that has a scope of transmission-reception, has a bounded aptitude. In order to increase this range, one has to appeal to those waves conceived in the heart. Therefore, the student has to concentrate on his own heart to receive the news beyond the ability of the brain. This heart- mediated level is what in truth should be called meditation (or mediation). The heart mediates for the brain and receives the waves beyond the brain's receptive power. I will elaborate on this level in another treatise.

Implicit to what I have presented on the subject of concentration is what I have previously termed as the principles of Harmony, Submission, and Unity. Concentration levels can also be classified following these same principles. Harmony is partially achieved when the student has chosen the subject and focuses his attention on it. The receiver (brain) harmonizes itself with those waves representing the subject while dismissing all other waves.   Submission is the state in which the student's E&M waves adjust themselves to those wavelengths of the subject.   Thus, in this manner the receiver submits to the subject.   Unity transpires when the student forgets everything else, including his/her own existence, and is only conscious of the waves of the subject.   My father and teacher Professor Sadegh Angha says:[11]

...*"If the knowledgeable mind had postulated the already-accomplished cognitions as ultimate, then certainly the last detail of civilization would have been attained and the truth of nature would have been announced to the world. But the true knowledgeable person, whose thoughts are established on disposition, deem an invariable, immutable, and infinite (or annihilated in infinity) center of character. Starting from this core of concentration, they instantly traverse an infinite and complete realm all around the circle of 360 degrees. Again from each hypothetical point of this realm, they traverse complete curves, thereby displaying the true mesh of perception (Angha's equivalent principle of Huygens' principle). While unable to reach the end of this realm ever, at any point, they perceive that tranquillity which is the outcome of those true foundations of disposition. Therefore, they make no mistake in projecting the outside world on the basis of these foundations. The advantage of this spiritual success is that no such scholar is childishly astounded by single discoveries and does not consider them extraordinary miracles. Furthermore, his studies of the doctrines of a discovery are intended for the preliminary comparisons or the fulfillment of the empty or doubtful parts of his own research. In fact, he employs the previous discoveries as a magnificent starting point.*[12]

In summary, I have discussed the mechanism for the propagation of the action potential along the nerve fiber. Present theories concerning this matter cannot explain the wavelike propagation of action potential. My assumption of the spiral path of the ions in the membrane ion channels leads to the inclusion of inductors in the membrane circuits. Consequently, the membrane circuits become complete radio circuits resulting in the oscillation of the current (and thus the action potential) through the membrane capacitor and the channel inductors. The Faraday induction of the current through the neighboring circuits results in the wavelike propagation of the action potential. I believe this explains the wavelike motion of the action potential through the nerve fibers.

The E&M wave nature of the nerve signals results in a wavelike communication and storage of information. Therefore, memory, mind, and consciousness are E&M waves. The brain (or the whole body) acts like a radio receiver and transmitter. It is on this foundation that I have discussed the levels of concentration.

CHAPTER4 – FIGURES

Figure 1. The central nervous system (CNS) is composed of the spinal cord and the brain. The spinal cord is shorter than the vertebral column. Nevertheless, the spinal nerves extend to the end of the vertebral canals as well as to the outside of the canal at the level of the corresponding vertebra. (using figure A in ref. 1 pg. 273)

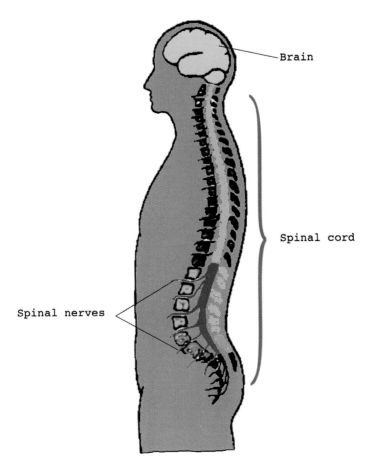

Figure 1.

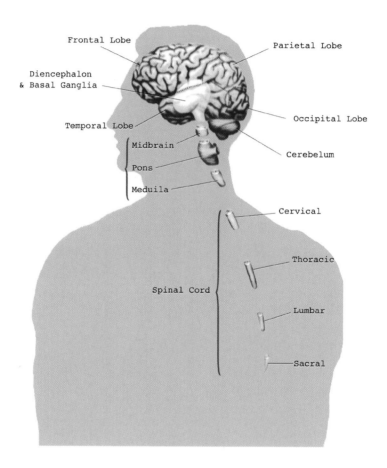

Figure 2a. The spinal cord, the brain stem, and the cerebral hemispheres.

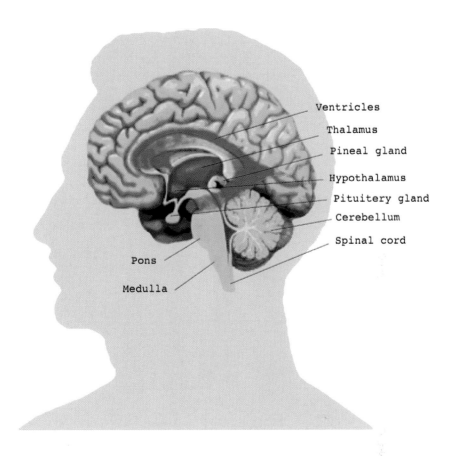

2b. A more detailed picture of the brain.

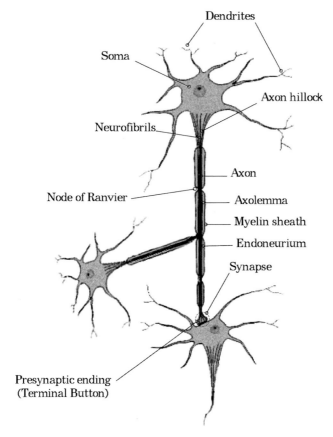

Figure 3- A schematic of a neuron.

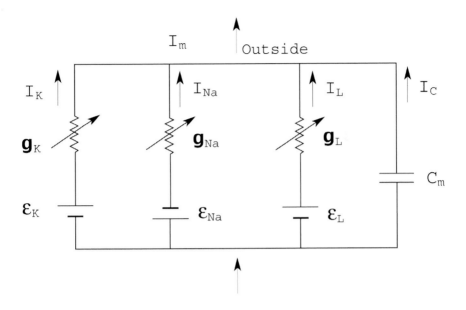

Figure 4- Parallel conductance model for the squid axon. The conductance's g_K and g_{Na} are voltage and time dependent and g_L is constant. The capacitance C_m is due to charge imbalance between the inner and outer layers of the membrane. The voltages ε_K, ε_{Na}, and ε_L are the resting potentials of the relevant ions.

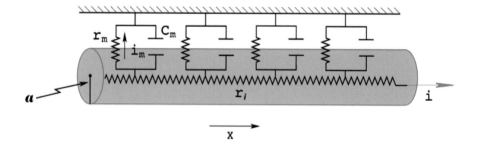

Figure 5. The parallel circuits of fig. 4
along the axon.

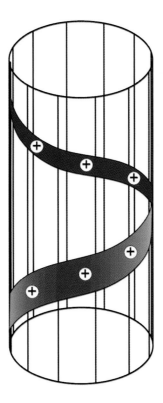

Figure 6- The helix model of the S_4 subunit of the brain Na$^+$ channel. The S_4 helix is proposed to undergo a rotation of 60° which results in a 5A° vertical displacement of positive charges. The positive charges are amino acid residues and are separated by 5A° too. Hence, each single rotation results in a positive charge emerging out of the membrane.

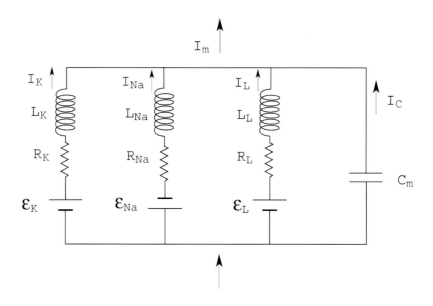

Figure 7.   The corrected parallel circuit.
The inductance's L_K, L_{Na}, and L_L are indicative

of the spiral path of the ions in their appropriate
channels.   The conductance's g_k, g_{Na}, and g_L are
substituted by resistance's R_K, R_{Na}, and R_L
respectively.   The voltages ε_K, ε_{Na}, and ε_L are the
resting potentials of the relevant ions.   The
membrane capacitance is shown by C_m.

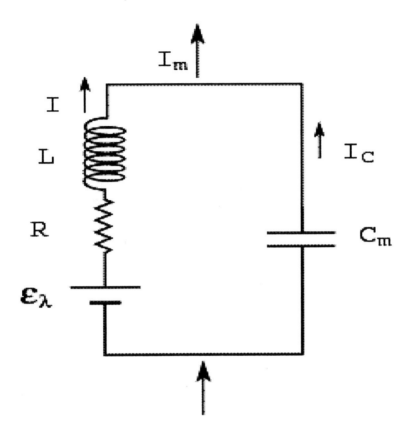

Figure 8. The equivalent circuit for the parallel circuit. The parameters L, R, and ε_λ are defined as follows:

$$\frac{1}{L} = \frac{1}{L_K} + \frac{1}{L_{Na}} + \frac{1}{L_L},$$

$$\frac{R}{L} = \frac{R_K}{L_K} = \frac{R_{Na}}{L_{Na}} = \frac{R_L}{L_L}, \text{ and}$$

$$\frac{\varepsilon_\lambda}{L} = L\left[\frac{\varepsilon_K}{L_K} - \frac{\varepsilon_{Na}}{L_{Na}} + \frac{\varepsilon_L}{L_L}\right]$$

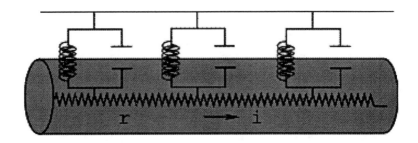

Figure 9.   Corrected parallel circuits along the axon.

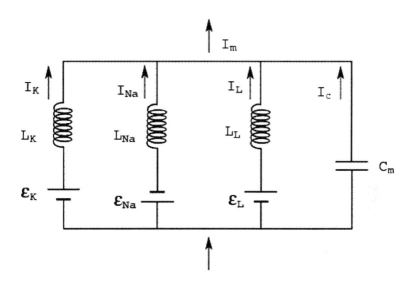

Figure 10. Corrected parallel circuit for superconducting channels, $R_K = R_{Na} = R_L = 0$.

APPENDIX I

The differential equation for the radiation of a particle is the same as Eq. (59) (chapter 3). In essence,

$$\nabla^2 \xi(\vec{r}) + \left[M^2 c^2 (1 - R_0/r)/\hbar^2 \right] \xi(\vec{r}) = 0, \qquad \text{(I-1)}$$

where $\xi(\vec{r}) = \vec{r} \cdot \vec{E}$ or $\vec{r} \cdot \vec{B}$ represents the E & M field of the particle. In reference 1 (chapter 3), Prof. Sadegh Angha shows that the electric and magnetic fields are found through the following Eqs.

$$\vec{E} = \left[4/i \; \hbar \; \ell(\ell+2) \right] \vec{\nabla} \times \vec{L} \; \xi(\vec{r}), \qquad \text{(I-2)}$$

$$\vec{B} = \left[4Mc/\hbar^2 \; \ell(\ell+2) \right] \vec{L} \; \xi(\vec{r}), \qquad \text{(I-3)}$$

which are Eqs. (1-50) and (1-49) of reference 1, respectively. Therefore once we have $\xi(\vec{r})$, we can then find the E & M field of the radiation energy of the particle. Going back to solve Eq. (I- 1), we use the standard method of separation of

variables.   Writing ∇^2 in spherical coordinates and
substituting $\xi(\vec{r})$ by $\left[\xi(\vec{r}) = R(r) P(\theta) \Phi(\phi)\right]$, we get
the following three differential equations:

$$(1/r^2) \; d\left[(r^2 \; dR / d\; r)\right]/d\; r - (\Lambda / r^2) R + \left[M^2 \; c^2 (1 - R_0 / r)\right.$$
$$\left. / \hbar^2 \right] R = 0, \qquad\qquad\qquad\qquad \text{(I-4)}$$

$$(1/\sin\theta) \; d\left[(\sin\theta) \; d\; P/d\; \theta\right]/d\; \theta - (J^2/\sin\theta)\; P + \Lambda P = 0, \quad \text{(I-5)}$$

and
$$d^2 \; \Phi/d\; \phi^2 + J^2 \; \Phi = 0 \qquad\qquad\qquad\qquad \text{(I-6)}$$

where Λ and J are constants independent of variables r, θ, and
ϕ. The solutions of the differential Eqs. (**I-5**) and (**I-6**) are
discussed in reference 1. Similar to the solutions proposed by
Prof. Sadegh Angha for the internal structure of particles, the
acceptable values of J and Λ are as follows:[1]

$$J = s /2, \qquad \text{with } s = 1, 2, 3, ... \qquad\qquad \text{(I-7)}$$
$$\Lambda = (\ell /2)\left[(\ell /2) + 1\right], \text{ with } \ell = 1, 2, 3, ... \qquad \text{(I-8)}$$

Again, similarly to reference 1, in order to preserve the single value of $\Phi(\phi)$ for ϕ. and $\phi + \pi$, we accept solutions of the following kind:

$$\xi(\overrightarrow{r}) = R(r)\, P\,(\theta)\left[\, \left|\text{Re }\Phi(\phi)\right| + i\, \left|\text{Im }\Phi(\phi)\right|\,\right]. \qquad (I\text{-}9)$$

In this case the half integer values of J are also acceptable. Then we can show that for specific values of s and the solutions to the angular part of $\xi(\overrightarrow{r})$ are

$$P_{l/2}^{s/2}\,(\theta)\, \Phi_{s/2}\,(\phi) \; = \; Y_{l/2}^{s/2}(\theta,\phi), \qquad (I\text{-}10)$$

where $Y_{l/2}^{s/2}\,(\theta,\phi)$ are the spherical harmonics.[14] In order to find the solution to the radial part of the differential equation, i.e. Eq. (I-4) we introduce a change of variable $(M\,c/\hbar)\, r \equiv x$. Then Eq. (I-4) changes to $(1/x^2)\, d\left[(x^2\, d\,R/d\,x)\right]/d\,x +$

$$\left[-\,(\Lambda/x^2) + 1 - (\beta/x)\,\right]R = 0,$$ where $\beta = McR_0/\hbar$. On the other hand since $R_0 = e^2/2\,M\,c^2$, then $\beta = e^2/2\,\hbar\,c$.

Differentiating with respect to "x" and multiplying by x^2, we have

$$x^2 (d^2R/dx^2) + (2\,x)(d\,R/d\,x) + \left\{ x^2 - \beta\,x \right.$$

$$\left. - (\ell/2) \left[(1/2)+1 \right] \right\} \; R = 0. \quad \text{(I-11)}$$

We look for a series solution of the Eq. **(I-11)**. Take

$$R\,(x) \;=\; \sum_{n=1}^{N} a_n\; x^{\,n + K}$$ and insert these R (x) into

(I-11) to find the indicial and recursion equations. After doing so, we find $k = \ell/2$, $a_1 = \beta a_0 /(\,\ell + 2\,)$ and $a_{n+2} = (\beta a_{n+1} - a_n)/\left[(n+2)(n+3+\ell) \right]$. The limiting value of n is

$N = m + \ell + 1$, with $m = 1, 2, 3\ldots\ldots$

Appendix II

The membrane current is perpendicular to the membrane itself and the internal current is along the axis of the cylindrical nerve fiber. Therefore, r_m is the resistance in the perpendicular direction to the membrane or to the axis. r_m, r_i, c_m, and i_m are the linear parameters; i.e. those for 1 cm along the fiber. On the other hand R_m, R_i, C_m, and I_m are parameters for 1 cm^2 area of their related surfaces. The parameters R_m, C_m, and I_m are for a strip of 1 cm^2 on the surface of the cylinder, while R_i is that for 1 cm^2 of the cross sectional area of the cylinder.

In order to find the equations converting one set of the parameters to the other, we approach as follows. Since the circumference of the outer layer of the cylinder is 2 πa , with "a" being the radius, in order to stack n of these circles to get an area of 1 cm^2, n has to be. $\frac{1}{2\pi a}$ For the case of membrane resistance, since the n resistors r_m have to be put together in parallel, then the total resistance R_m is

$$R_m = \frac{r_m}{n} = 2 \pi a \, r_{m.}$$
(II - 1)

For the case of membrane capacitance, the n capacitors c_m are put together in parallel to yield the net capacitance C_m. Therefore

$$C_m = n \, c_m = \frac{C_m}{2\pi \, a}.$$
(II - 2)

In the case of the membrane current, we have to put n parallel i_m's to get I_m. Thus

$$I_m = n \, i_m = \frac{i_m}{2\pi \, a}.$$
(II - 3)

For the case of the internal resistance since the current passes through the whole surface of area πa^2 in order to get an area of 1 cm^2, N of these disks have to be stacked beside each other. Hence

$$N = \frac{1}{\pi a^2}.$$
(II - 4)

Since these N disks are in series, then

$$R_i = N r_i = \frac{r_i}{\pi a^2}. \qquad\qquad \text{(II - 5)}$$

Finally for the internal current since there are N = πa^2 of 1 cm^2 areas in the surface of one disk, then the current passing through one disk is

$$I_d = N I_i = \pi a^2 I_i \qquad\qquad \text{(II - 6)}$$

but no matter how many of these disks are stacked together since the disks are in series the net current is still the same. Thus

$$i_i = \pi a^2 I_i. \qquad\qquad \text{(II - 7)}$$

Appendix III

I have applied the condition of equality of wavelengths of interacting systems to phonon and energy gap in conventional superconductors, and to phonon, energy gap, and de Broglie wave of the conduction electron in high-T_c superconductors. The resulting T_c values are relatively close to the experimental ones. Applying this condition, the thermodynamic critical magnetic field of type I superconductors and the lower and upper critical fields of type II superconductors were calculated. The same procedure was used for high-T_c superconductors . The present calculation of the normal state Sumerfeld constant, γ_n results in a general expression which is 9 % smaller than the classical one. The superconducting γ_c at T_c was calculated and the resulting jump in the electronic specific heat was determined. There is relatively good agreement between the present and experimental results.

III-1. INTRODUCTION

The electrical transport properties of matter seem far from being understood. Among these properties, superconductivity is one of the most interesting phenomenon. Since the discovery of superconductivity in 1911, numerous physicists have tried to propose theoretical models to describe the mechanism of this phenomenon. Perhaps the most successful of these models is the microscopic BCS theory[13]. However after the advent of high-T_c superconductors, questions emerged about the global applicability of this theoretical model[14].

In this appendix I present a new approach to the theoretical modeling of superconductivity. For conventional superconductors I will show that superconductivity occurs whenever the wavelength of the energy released during the formation of the electron-pair, i.e. energy gap, is equal to the phonon wavelength. For high-T_c superconductors also the Fermi energy should be in harmony with (have the same wavelength as) with the energy gap and the phonons.

In the context of the present approach it will be shown that isotope effect[15] exists for both types of superconductors. The present magnitude of α (in $T_c \propto M^\alpha$), is 0.667 and 0.571 for conventional and high-T_c superconductors respectively.

A magnetic field, H increases the phonon energy and thus decreases the phonon wavelength. In a superconductor (initially at $T < T_c$) once the phonon wavelength is lowered to that of the energy gap, i.e. they are in harmony, the energy of the gap is reabsorbed from the environment and transferred to the electron-pair thus breaking the pair. The magnetic field at which this occurs is the thermodynamic critical magnetic field, H_C. Using this H_C and the Ginzburg-Landau parameter, κ [15,16] the lower and upper critical fields, H_{c1} and H_{c2}[15,16] are calculated. The present calculated magnitudes of H_C, for type I superconductors, and those of H_{c1} and H_{c2} for conventional and high-T_c type II superconductors[15] agree relatively well with the experimental results.

The application of the condition of harmony (equality of wavelengths) of the thermal energy of electrons with their de Broglie energy results in a Sumerfeld constant, γ_n,[17,18] which is about 9 % smaller than its classical value. The inclusion of the extra energy of the gap, given off by the electron-pair at T_c, in the electronic thermal energy results in the superconducting Sumerfeld constant γ_s. The relative jump in electronic specific heat[15,16] $\delta\gamma/\gamma_n$ is calculated. The agreement between the present $\delta\gamma/\gamma_n$'s and experiment is much better than that between the BCS weak coupling results, $\left[(\delta\gamma / \gamma_n) = 1.43 \right]$, [15,16] and experiment.

Finally based upon the thesis that in high-T_c superconductors, at T_c, there should exist harmony between the phonons, the energy gap, and the Fermi energy, I investigate the possibility of the occurrence of a room temperature superconductor.

III-2. TRANSITION TEMPERATURE (T_c)

III-2.1 Conventional Superconductors

The Debye low temperature approximation of the phonon energy[17,18] is

$$U_{ph} = \frac{3\,\pi^4}{5}\, k_B\, T \left(\frac{T}{\theta_D}\right)^3 \qquad \text{(III-1)}$$

In Debye model the speed of the phonon wave is taken to be the same as that of sound (v_s) in the environment[17]. Considering, $U_{ph} = \hbar\,\omega_{ph}$, and using the equation $\lambda_{ph} = \frac{2\,\pi\,v_s}{\omega_{ph}} = \frac{h\,v_s}{U_{ph}}$, the wavelength of this wave is

$$\lambda_{ph} = \frac{5\,h\,v_s\,\theta_D{}^3}{3\,\pi^4\,k_B\,T^4}\,, \qquad \text{(III-2)}$$

where λ_{ph} is the phonon wavelength.

Taking the speed of the radiated waves by the conduction electrons to be the same as the Fermi velocity, v_F, the wavelength of the radiated wave of energy, 2Δ, can similarly be found. We have

$$\lambda_{gap} = \frac{h\, v_F}{2\Delta} \,,\qquad\qquad\text{(III-3)}$$

with λ_{gap} being the wavelength of the wave with energy equal to the energy gap, $2\Delta^{13,15}$.

In case of conventional superconductors my model of the occurrence of superconductivity is as follows. Although the formation of the electron–pair is possible at any temperature, at higher temperatures where λ_{ph} is smaller than λ_{gap}, the bond formed by two conduction electrons is broken by the phonons. The onset of superconductivity occurs, at T_c, when

$$\lambda_{ph} = \lambda_{gap} \,.\qquad\qquad\text{(III-4)}$$

Using Eqs. (III-2) and (III-3), we have

$$T_c^{\,4} = \frac{10\,\Delta\, v_s\, \theta_D^{\,3}}{3\pi^4\, k_B\, v_F} \,.\qquad\qquad\text{(III-5)}$$

According to BCS theory[13] for conventional superconductors $2\Delta \approx 3.5 \ k_B \ T_c$ [15]. In general we take $2\Delta = \eta k_B \ T_c$. In that case

$$T_c = \left[\frac{5 \eta \ v_s}{3\pi^4 \ v_F} \right]^{1/3} \theta_D. \qquad \text{(III-6)}$$

For $T \leq T_c$, the electrons of the pair are stably bound and thus the system remains in its superconducting state. By the Bohm $-$ Staver relation[18] we have

$$\frac{v_s}{v_F} = \left(\frac{Z \ m_e}{3 \ M} \right)^{1/2} .$$

Here Z is the number of the valence electrons and M is the atomic mass. Substituting $\frac{v_s}{v_F}$ in Eq. (III-6) from above, taking $\eta = 3.5$ which is determined experimentally[15], and after simplification we have

$$T_c = 9.31 \times 10^{-2} \left(\frac{Z}{A} \right)^{1/6} \theta_D, \qquad \text{(III-7)}$$

where A is the atomic number.

Table **I** shows the experimental T_c[15,13] and

those from Eq. (III-7) for some superconducting

elements and alloys. For tungsten, W, the two T_c

values differ by three orders of magnitude. For Hf

and Ir, the two series of values differ by two

orders of magnitude. It can be seen that the two

series of T_c values for Hg, In, La, Nb, Pb, Sn, Ta,

Th, Tl, approximate each other closely. For the

rest of the elements of Table **I** the two T_c values

differ by one order of magnitude. Table **I** also

shows the magnitudes of λ_{ph} ($= \lambda_{gap}$) at T_c for

some elements. Typical values of these

wavelengths are $\lambda_{ph} = \lambda_{gap} \approx 1 \times 10^{-4}$ cm .

One may wonder what the effects are of the

thermal motion of the electron and the motion of

the electron at the Fermi level on T_c of the

conventional superconductors. The wavelength of

the de Broglie wave due to the thermal energy of the electron λ Th. e is

$$\lambda_{\text{Th. e}} = \frac{h\,v_F}{\left(\frac{1}{2}\,\gamma\,T_c^{\,2}\right)},\qquad\qquad\text{(III-8)}$$

where γ is the Sumerfeld constant[17,18]. Taking v_F $\approx$ 1.5 X 10^8 cm s^{-1} [18,19], γ = 10 mJmol^{-1} K^{-2} [15,17,18], and T_c = 10 K[15,17,18] we obtain $\lambda_{\text{Th. e}}$ $\approx$ 1 X 10^{-1} cm s^{-1} which is about 1000 times larger than λ ph or λ gap ($\approx$1 X 10^{-4} cm).

Therefore due to this disharmony in conventional superconductors the thermal motion of the electron does not contribute to the superconductivity. On the other hand the de Broglie wavelength, λc.e, due to the Fermi energy of the electron at the conduction band, is

$$\lambda_{\text{c.e}} = \frac{h}{m_e\,v_F},\qquad\qquad\text{(III-9)}$$

where λc.e is the wavelength of the conduction electron at Fermi level. Here λc.e has an approximate upper limit of 1×10^{-7} cm. This is about 1000 times smaller than λ_{ph} or λ_{gap}.

Consequently, at the superconducting transition temperature T_c neither the electronic thermal nor the Fermi de Broglie waves are in harmony with the gap or the phonon waves. Thus they do not contribute to the determination of the superconducting transition temperature T_c.

Since $\theta_D \propto v_s \propto M^{-1/2}$, from Eq.(III-6) we have

$$T_c \propto M^{-2/3}, \qquad\qquad\qquad (III-10)$$

which shows the effect of the isotopic mass on T_c[15,16,19,20].Thus for conventional superconductors the present approach confirms the existence of the isotope effect, i.e. $T_c \propto M^{-\alpha}$, with $\alpha = 0.667$.

The original BCS model predicted $\alpha = 0.5$[15,17].

In the present context the dependence of T_c on isotopic mass could be accounted for as follows. The nuclear mass affects the phonon wavelength, thus controlling T_c , at which the phonon and the gap are in harmony.

III-2.2 High-T_c Superconductors

For high-T_c superconductors at the transition temperature, T_c, I claim that the energy gap, the phonons , and the de Broglie wave of the electrons at the Fermi level all have to be in harmony. Therefore in addition to the previous condition of harmony between phonons and the energy gap the Fermi energy also must be in harmony with these waves. Perhaps this is the main difference between the conventional and high-T_c superconductors[15,19,20]. Thus to find the T_c of these superconductors[14,16,19,20] we require $\lambda_{ph} = \lambda_{gap} = \lambda_{c.e}$. Pursuing this, we have

$$\frac{h\,v_s}{\left(U_{ph}\right)_c} = \frac{h\,v_F}{\eta k_B\,T_c} = \frac{h}{m_e\,v_F} \qquad \text{(III-11)}$$

where $\left(U_{ph}\right)_c$ is the phonon energy at T_c. Solving the system of above two equations for v_F and T_c we have

$$v_F = \left[\frac{5\,\eta^4\,v_s}{3\pi^4}\right]^{1/7} \left(\frac{k_s\,\theta_D}{m_e}\right)^{3/7},\qquad\qquad\text{(III-12)}$$

$$T_c = \left[\frac{25\,\eta\,m_e\,v_s^2}{9\,\pi^8\,k_B}\right]^{1/7}\theta_D^{6/7}.\qquad\qquad\text{(III-13)}$$

Note that Eq. (III-13) is the same as Eq. (III-6), with its v_F substituted from Eq. (III-12).

One of the many unique properties of high-T_c superconductors is their unconventionally large energy gap value $\eta\,k_B\,T_c$[16,19-24]. A typical experimental value is $\eta\,k_B\,T_c \approx 7\,k_B\,T_c$[16,19-24]. The value of $\eta \approx 7$ is about twice that of conventional superconductors, or that from BCS theory[13,15,16]. We assume the velocity of sound to remain at the same order of magnitude as that in conventional superconductors, i.e. $v_s \approx 5 \times 10^5$ cm s^{-1}[25-27].

Table **II** shows the reported[16,23,24,28-30], as well as the calculated, values of T_c and v_F for some high–T_c superconductors. Except for two samples, the theoretical and experimental T_c's have the same order of magnitude. Another characteristic of the high–T_c superconductors is their relatively lower value of the Fermi velocity, v_F, i.e. $v_F \approx 1 \times 10^7$ cm s^{-1}[16,19,24,30]. As Table II shows our calculated values of v_F are only 1 – 35 % different than the reported values. From Eq. (III-13), $T_c \propto M^{-4/7}$ indicating $\alpha = 0.571$ in high–T_c superconductors[16,19,20]. In conventional superconductors only two waves must be in harmony. On the other hand in high–T_c superconductors the harmony must occur among three waves. This requirement reduces the strength of coupling of the phonons with electron-pair, i.e. the energy gap. Therefore the electron-phonon coupling in high–T_c superconductors is weaker than that in conventional superconductors. Also for the compounds of Table **II**, we have 7.03×10^{-7} cm $\leq \lambda_{ph} = \lambda_{gap} = \lambda_{c.e} \leq 11.0 \times 10^{-7}$ cm.

III -3. THE CRITICAL MAGNETIC FIELDS

III -3.1 Conventional Superconductors

The transition to the superconducting state is a second order transition in which there is no latent heat[15]. Thus the energy of the gap, released after the electron-pair is formed, is delivered to the environment inside the superconductor. This energy is manifested as a jump in the electronic thermal energy or in particular that in the electronic specific heat, γ. Once the temperature, T ($< T_c$), of a superconductor is brought up to the transition temperature T_c , an electron exposed to the phonons delivers to the phonons that part of the energy gap which it received after the formation of the pairs. The presence of phonons is necessary because they mediate the transfer of the gap energy from the pair to the individual electrons and vice versa. The phonons, in fact act as catalyzers.

In order to arrive at the magnitude for the critical magnetic fields of both classes of superconductors,

we approach as follows. An increase in the
magnetic field H produces an increase in the
energy of the phonons, thereby decreasing their
wavelength. At a temperature $T < T_c$ once the
number of phonons, of energy $(U_{ph})_c$, equals the
number of electron-pairs then the phonons
reabsorb the gap energy from the single-electrons
and deliver it to the pairs thus breaking them and
driving the system to normal conductivity.
Phonons of energy $(U_{ph})_c$ are essential because
only these phonons are in harmony with the energy
gap. Thus only these phonons can reabsorb the gap
energy from the single-electrons. The energy,
$\delta U_{ph} = (U_{ph})_c - U_{ph}$, needed to bring a phonon
at temperature T $(< T_c)$ to that at temperature T_c
is

$$\delta U_{ph} = (U_{ph})_c \left[1 - \frac{U_{ph}}{(U_{ph})_c} \right],$$

or

$$\delta U_{ph} = \frac{3\pi^4}{5} k_B T_c \left(\frac{T_c}{\theta_D} \right)^3 \left[1 - \left(\frac{T}{T_c} \right)^4 \right], \quad \text{(III-14)}$$

There are as many as $n_s = n\left[1-\left(\frac{T}{T_c}\right)^4\right]$ electron-pairs per unit volume of the system at $T \leq T_c$[15,16]. Thus the total energy per unit volume, $\frac{H_c^2}{8\pi}$ needed to drive the system out of superconductivity is

$$\frac{H_c^2}{8\pi} = \frac{3\pi^4}{5} n\ k_B T_c \left(\frac{T_c}{\theta_D}\right)^3 \left[1-\left(\frac{T}{T_c}\right)^4\right]^2$$

or

$$H_c(T) = \left[\frac{24\ \pi^5}{5} n\ k_B\ T_c \left(\frac{T_c}{\theta_D}\right)^3\right]^{1/2} \left[1-\left(\frac{T}{T_c}\right)^4\right].$$
$$\text{(III–15)}$$

The thermodynamic critical magnetic field at $T = 0$ is

$$H_c(0) = \left[\frac{24\ \pi^5}{5} n\ k_B\ T_c \left(\frac{T_c}{\theta_D}\right)^3\right]^{1/2}. \qquad \text{(III-16)}$$

Table **III** shows the experimental values of $H_c(0)$ [15,17,18] as well as those calculated from Eq. (III-16) for some superconducting elements. Generally speaking, there is relatively good agreement between the two sets of results. Table **IV** shows the experimental[16] values of $H_c(0)$ and our calculated values of $H_c(0)$ and $H_{c2}(0)$ for some type II superconductors.

III-3.2   High-T_c Superconductors

To find the lower critical field, H_{c1} (T), of high-T_c superconductors I use the same equation for H_c (T) as I have used for conventional superconductors. Thus, once again for H_{c1} (T), when there are as many phonons of energy $(U_{ph})_c$, as there are electron-pairs, the thermodynamic critical field is reached. Table **V** shows the thermodynamic critical field, H_c (0) for some high-T_c superconductors. The Ginzburg - Landau parameter, κ, of these compounds[31-33] is also shown in this table. Using these κ 's and the equation[16]

$$H_{c1} \approx \frac{H_c}{\sqrt{2}\,\kappa} \ln \kappa, \qquad\qquad (III-17)$$

I have derived the $H_{c1}(0)$ of these compounds. For $YBa_2Cu_4O_8$ the directional average of H_{c1} (0) is 172 Oe[16] which is very close to the lower limit of the present value of 174 Oe $<$ H_{c1} (0) $<$ 239 Oe for this compound .

To find the upper critical field, H_{c2} (T) of high-T_c superconductors, I use the following approach.   Again the energy, δU_{ph}, needed to bring a phonon to the critical energy satisfies the equation

$$\delta \ U_{ph} = \left(U_{ph}\right)_c \left[1 - \frac{U_{ph}}{\left(U_{ph}\right)_c} \right].$$

.

We could follow the same steps as before and use the fact that $\frac{U_{ph}}{\left(U_{ph}\right)_c} = \left(\frac{T}{T_c}\right)^4$. However let's elaborate on this. From Eq. (III-11) we have

$$\eta \ k_B \ T = \frac{v_F}{v_s} \left(U_{ph}\right)_c .$$

Assuming $50 \ K < T_c < 100 \ K^{28}$ for these superconductors, for temperatures around T_c we can write[34]

$$\eta \ k_B \ T_c \approx \frac{v_F}{v_s} \ U_{ph} . \qquad\qquad\qquad \text{(III-19)}$$

Therefore

$$\frac{U_{ph}}{\left(U_{ph}\right)_c} \approx \frac{T}{T_c} , \qquad\qquad\qquad \text{(III-20)}$$

and, consequently,

$$\delta\, U_{ph} \approx \left(U_{ph}\right)_c \left[1 - \frac{T}{T_c}\right] . \qquad\qquad \text{(III-21)}$$

On the other hand according to Eq. (III-11), for high-T_c superconductors at T_c the electrons at the Fermi energy are also in harmony with phonons. Thus phonons of energy $\left(U_{ph}\right)_c$ will be absorbed by the individual conduction electrons as well as by the electron-pairs. Therefore to quench all traces of superconductivity, all of the phonons must reach the energy $\left(U_{ph}\right)_c$. This must be the case to compensate for energy exchange with the individual electrons in addition to that with the electron-pairs. Consequently the energy found in Eq. (III-21) times the total number of the phonons per unit volume, n_{ph}, is, what I call, the upper thermodynamic energy per unit volume, $\dfrac{H_{cu}^{2}}{8\,\pi}$ needed to completely quench all traces of the superconductivity. We have

$$H_{cU} = \left[\frac{24 \ \pi^5 \ D}{5 \ M} N_A \ k_B \ T_c \left(\frac{T_c}{\theta_D} \right)^3 \right]^{1/2} \left[1 - \frac{T}{T_c} \right]^{1/2}$$

(III-22)

The experimental results on powders of YBa$_2$Cu$_3$O$_{7-\delta}$ show that $H^{\|}_{c\,2} \propto \left[1 - \frac{T}{T_c} \right]^{1/2}$ [35].

Also it has been reported that within the experimental error, $H_{c\,2}$ (T) rises vertically in the H-T plane[35]. These facts are in agreement with Eq. (III-22). From this equation we have

$$H_{cU} (0) = \left[\frac{24 \ \pi^5 \ D}{5 \ M} N_A \ k_B \ T_c \left(\frac{T_c}{\theta_D} \right)^3 \right]^{1/2}$$

(III-23)

Table **V** also shows the H$_{cU}$ (0) values for some high-T_c superconducting compounds. The H$_{c2}$ (0) values can be found using the equation[16]

$$H_{c2} \approx \sqrt{2} \ \kappa \ H_c.$$

(III-24)

The upper critical fields, H$_{c2}$ (0) as large as 670 Tesla have been estimated for some high-T_c superconductors[16]. This is within the range of our values of the H_{c2} (0) of the compounds shown in Table **V**.

III-4. THE ELECTRONIC SPECIFIC

HEAT

III-4.1   The Normal State

The electronic specific heat of normal state conductors and the jump in the specific heat of superconductors also can be derived from the condition of harmony. In essence the transfer of energy to the electron takes place while the electron is in harmony with the incoming wave. This indicates that the magnitude of the energy absorbed by an electron is determined by the wavelength of the de Broglie wave of the electron itself. This also is the reason for the quantized exchanges of energy (i.e. frequency) and momentum (i.e. wavelength) in interactions[36].

In the case of the normal electronic specific heat the macroscopic thermal energy of the wave is $3\,k_B\,T$. The speed of this wave when it is free being v_F results in $\lambda_{Th.\,e} = \dfrac{h\,v_F}{3\,k_B\,T}$. On the other hand, the wavelength of the electron's de Broglie wave should be the same as the above. Using the relations: $\lambda \omega = v$ and $\hbar \omega = m v^2$ for the de Broglie wave in general for any particle we can write

$$\hbar \omega_n = \frac{(h/\lambda)^2}{m} , \qquad \text{(III-25)}$$

where $\hbar \omega_n$ is the energy of the de Broglie wave. Using $\lambda_{Th.e} = \dfrac{h \, v_F}{3 \, k_B \, T}$, the (thermal) de Broglie energy of the electron at temperature T is

$$\hbar \omega_n = \frac{(3 \, k_B \, T)^2}{m_e \, v_F^2} , \qquad \text{(III-26)}$$

Half of this energy is equal to the thermal kinetic energy of the electron which is defined as $\frac{1}{2}\gamma_n \, T^2$. Therefore we have

$$\gamma_n = \frac{9 \, k_B^2}{m \, v_F^2} \qquad \text{(III-27)}$$

This is about 9 % lower than the classical value of the Sumerfeld constant, $\gamma_n = \dfrac{\pi^2 \, k_B^2}{m \, v_F^2}$ [17].

III-4.2 The Superconducting State

In a superconductor at the transition temperature, T_c the energy, $\eta\ k_B\ T_c$ released by the formation of an electron-pair also contributes to the electronic thermal energy. Similar to the normal conductivity case, the energy contributed by $\eta\ k_B\ T_c$ to the thermal energy of the electron is

$$\hbar\ \Omega\ =\ \frac{(\eta\ k_B\ T_c\ )^2}{m\ v_F^{\,2}} \qquad\qquad \text{(III-28)}$$

Therefore the total energy of the thermal de Broglie wave of the electron at T_c is

$$\hbar\ \omega_s\ =\ \frac{(\eta^2 + 9)(k_B\ T_c)^2}{m\ v_F^{\,2}} \qquad\qquad \text{(III-29)}$$

Again half of this energy is equal to the kinetic energy of the electron or $\frac{1}{2}\gamma_s\ T_c^{\,2}$; therefore

$$\gamma_s\ =\ \frac{(\eta^2 + 9)k_B^{\,2}}{m\ v_F^{\,2}} \qquad\qquad \text{(III-30)}$$

Consequently the jump in the electronic specific heat at the superconducting transition temperature

T_c is

$$\frac{\gamma_s - \gamma_n}{\gamma_n} = \frac{\eta^2}{9}.$$ 　　　　　　(III-31)

Table **VI** shows the experimental results[16] of the relative jump in the electronic specific heat and those from Eq. (III-31) for some elements. Taking $\eta = 7$ for high-T_c superconductors, Eq. (III-31) results in $\frac{\eta^2}{9} = 5.4$. Values of $\frac{\gamma_s - \gamma_n}{\gamma_n} = 2\text{-}10$ have been reported for $La_{1.85} Sr_{0.15} CuO_4$[33].

III-5. CONCLUSIONS AND DISCUSSION

In conclusion I have applied the condition of harmony to superconductivity. In essence for conventional superconductors at T_c the wavelength of the energy gap is equal to that of the phonon. For high-T_c superconductors, at T_c, the wavelength of the Fermi energy is also equal to the previous two wavelengths. The theoretical values of the transition temperature, T_c, for both the conventional and high-T_c superconductors agree well with the experimental results. Our magnitudes of H_c for type I superconductors, and H_{c1} and H_{c2} for both classes of superconductors, agree well with the experimental results.

The harmony of the electron's de Broglie wave and the electronic thermal energy $3 k_B T$ results in a Sumerfeld constant, γ_n, which values about 9% from its classical value. The inclusion of the energy earned from that of the gap, $\eta k_B T_c$, in the electron's thermal de Broglie wave energy results in the superconducting Sumerfeld constant

γ_s. Using the γ_s and γ_n, I calculated the relative jump in the electronic specific heat, $\delta\gamma / \gamma_n$.

Finally let's look at a possible characteristic of room temperature superconductors. Similar to the high-T_c case, we assume that for room temperature superconductors, at T_c, the Fermi energy, the phonon, and the energy gap are all in harmony. As in Eq. (III-11), we have

$$\frac{h \, v_s}{(U_{ph})_c} = \frac{h \, v_F}{\eta \, k_B \, T_c} = \frac{h}{m_e \, v_F}$$

with $(U_{ph})_c \approx 3 k_B T_c$ because the T_c is supposed to be in the room temperature range.

Solving this set of two equations for v_s and v_F we have

$$v_s = \left(\frac{9 \, k_B \, T_c}{\eta \, m_e}\right)^{1/2} \qquad\qquad \text{(III-32)}$$

and

$$v_F = \left(\frac{\eta\, k_B\, T_c}{m_e}\right)^{1/2} .$$ (III-33)

Taking T_c = 330 K and η = 7, we have v_s = 7.07 X 10^4 ms^{-1} and v_F = 1.7 X 10^5 ms^{-1}. Whereas the Fermi velocity has the typical value of that in high-T_c superconductors, the speed of sound is about 10-20 times higher than its typical value in conventional as well as in high-T_c superconductors. Therefore in our search to find the room temperature superconductor perhaps we should seek those high-T_c superconductors wherein the speed of sound is 10-20 time higher than its typical value of 5 X 10^3 ms^{-1}.

I have not yet discussed the nature of the energy gap and why two electrons bond together and form a pair. However the preliminary results of my research concerning these questions follows. The formation of the pair and the magnitude of the energy gap are intimately related to the thermal history and phase structure of the superconducting material. My suggested mechanism of the formation for the electron-pair will be presented in a future paper.

Table **I** The experimental and theoretical transition temperature, T_c and the phonon (energy gap) wavelength , λ_{ph} ($= \lambda_{gap}$), for some superconducting elements and alloys.

Element or Alloy	$T_c{}^a$ (K)	$T_c{}^b$ (K)	λ ph $(=\lambda_{gap})^c$ 10^{-4} cm
Al	1.196	27.7	1.0
Cd	0.56	9.94	2.2
Ga	1.091	12.7	2.1
Hf	0.09	12.5	...
Hg	4.15	3.11	6.9
In	3.40	5.48	4.3
Ir	0.14	20.5	...
La	4.9	6.98	...
Mo	0.92	26.4	...
Nb	9.26	15.7	1.2
Os	0.655	24.5	...
Pb	7.19	4.52	5.5

Element or Alloy	T_c^a (K)	T_c^b (K)	λ ph $(=\lambda_{gap})^c$ 10^{-4} cm
Re	1.698	23.2	...
Ru	0.49	32.6	...
Sn	3.27	10.6	2.4
Ta	4.48	12.3	...
Th	1.368	7.71	...
Ti	0.39	25.8	...
Tl	2.39	3.01	7.7
V	5.30	24.0	...
W	0.012	21.0	...
Zn	0.875	17.0	1.5
Zr	0.65	16.1	...
NbN	17.3	18.7	...
ZrN	10.7	20.7	...
MoC	14.3	38.8	...
NbC	11.6	22.0	...

Element or Alloy	T_c^a (K)	T_c^b (K)	λ ph $(=\lambda_{gap})^c$ 10^{-4} cm
Nb_3 Ge	23.2	17.3	...
V_3 Ga	16.5	19.0	...
V_2 Hf	9.4 1	10.6	...
$PbMo_6$ S_8	15.3	25.3	...
$PbMo_6$ Se_8	6.7	16.6	...

[a] References 15,16,17 , and 18.

[b] The transition temperature , T_c, is calculated using the equation $T_c = 9.31 \times 10^{-2} \left(\dfrac{Z}{A} \right)^{1/6} \theta_D$ where the Debye temperetures, θ_D were taken from reference 17.

[c] The Phonon an d energy gap wavelengths, which are equal at T_c , are calculated from the equation

$$\lambda_{ph} = \lambda_{gap} \approx \frac{h \, v_F}{3.5 \, k_B \, T_c} \, .$$

Table **I I** The reported and calculated transition temperature ,T_c and the Fermi velocity for some high-T_c superconductors.

Compound	$T_c{}^a$ (K)	$v_F{}^b$ $(10^7$ cm s$^{-1})$	$\theta_D{}^a$ (K)	$v_F{}^c$ $(10^7$ cm s$^{-1})$	$T_c{}^d$ (K)
Ba$_{1-x}$ K$_x$ Bi O$_3$	25-34	0.714	~ 200	0.665	42
Ba Pb$_{1-x}$ Bi$_x$ O$_3$	13	~1.0	195	0.657	41
Bi$_2$ Sr$_2$ Ca$_{n-1}$ Cu$_n$ O$_y{}^e$	10,85,100	0.713	230-290	0.706-0.779	47-57
Bi Sr Ca Cu$_2$ O$_{10}$	85	0.713	550	1.03	99
La$_{1.85}$ Ba$_{0.15}$ Cu O$_4$	39	~ 1.0	350-400	0.845-0.895	67-75
La$_{2-x}$ Sr$_x$ Cu O$_4$	40	0.817	400-500	0.895-0.980	75-91
La$_{1.85}$ Sr$_{0.15}$ Cu O$_4$	37	1.04	285-450	0.774-0.941	56-83
Y Ba$_2$ Cu$_3$ O$_{6,7}$	89-103	~1.0	300-500	0.791-0.984	59-91

[a] References 16,23,28, and 29.

[b] The Fermi Velocity, v_F is either taken from references 19, 24, 29, and 30 or calculated from $v_F = \left(\dfrac{h}{m}\right)(3\,\pi^2\,n)^{1/3}$ where n is reported by reference 28.

[c] The Fermi Velocity, v_F is calculated from

$$v_F = \left[\frac{5\,\eta^4\,v_s}{3\pi^4}\right]^{1/7}\left[\frac{k_B\,\theta_D{}^3}{m_e}\right]^{3/7}.$$

d The T_c is calculated from $T_c = \dfrac{25\,\eta\,m_e\,v_s^{\,2}}{9\,\pi^8\,k_B}\,\theta_D^{\,6/7}$, where $\eta = 7$ and $v_s = 5 \times 10^5\,\text{cm s}^{-1}$.

e The subscript n = 1, 2, and 3.

Table III The experimental and calculated critical magnetic field of some superconducting elements.

Element	n^a 10^{22} (cm^{-3})	H_c^b (Oe)	H_c^c (Oe)
Al	18.1	99	31
Cd	9.27	30	14
Ga	15.3	51	60
Hf	17.7	...	0.39
Hg	8.12	411	3617
In	11.5	293	1573
Ir	26.4	19	0.53
La	8.7	798	1884
Mo	32	98	23
Nb	5.56	1980	1996
Os	32.6	65	10
Pb	13.2	803	7860
Re	25.5	198	73.5
Ru	7.36	66	2.0

Element	n^a 10^{22} (cm^{-3})	H_c^b (Oe)	H_c^c (Oe)
Sn	14.8	305	847
Ta	27.6	830	1277
Th	12.1	162	141
Ti	19.8	100	4.0
Tl	10.5	171	1198
V	24.0	1020	836
Zn	13.2	53	21
Zr	17.1	47	16

[a] The concentration of the electrons, n, was calculated

using the equation $n = \dfrac{ZD}{M} N_A$, where Z is the most

frequent valence number, D is the mass density, M is the

atomic mass, and N_A is Avagadro's number.

[b] References 15,17, and 18.

^cThe thermodynamic critical magnetic field at T = 0 K, H_c

(0), was calculated using the equation

$$H_c\,(0) = \left[\,\frac{24\,\pi^5}{5}\,n\,k_B\,T_c\left(\frac{T_c}{\theta_D}\right)^3\,\right]^{1/2}$$

Table IV The experimental values of the upper critical

fields at T = 0, H_{c2} (0), and the theoretical values of the

thermodynamic and upper critical fields at T = 0, H_c (0) and

H_{c2} (0), of some type II superconducting alloys.

Alloy	H_{c2}[a] (Tesla)	H_c[b] (Tesla)	H_{c2}[c] (Tesla)
NbN	47	0.58	15.7
ZrN	0.3	0.17	0.36
MoC	9.8	0.16	1.9
NbC	2.0	0.23	1.3
$Nb_3 Ge$	38	2.1	51
$V_3 Ga$	27	0.26	5.3
$V_3 Si$	25	1.27	25
$V_2 Hf$	20	0.80	13.8
$PbMo_6 S_8$	60	0.64	19.6
$PbMo_6 Se_8$	7	0.21	2.1

[a] Reference 16.

[b]
The thermodynamic critical magnetic field at $T = 0$ K,

H_c (0), was calculated using the equation

$$H_c (0) = \left[\frac{24 \pi^5}{5} n k_B T_c \left(\frac{T_c}{\theta_D} \right)^3 \right]^{1/2}$$

[c]
In order to get an estimate of H_{c2} (0) of these alloys the

following approach was taken . The penetration depth was

taken as $\lambda = 500$ A° . The coherence length, x, was

calculates through the equation $H_{c2} = \frac{\Phi_0}{2 \pi \xi^2}$, with

$\Phi_0 = \frac{hc}{2e} = 2.06 \times 10^{-7}$ G cm^2, using the experimental

H_{c2} (0) of column 2 (Reference 18). with the above values

o f λ and ξ, the Ginzburg -Landau parameter, $k = \frac{\lambda}{\xi}$,

was calculated . Finally using the above values of k, the

values H_{c2} (0) of the alloys of this table were estimated

through the equation $H_{c2} = \sqrt{2} \kappa H_c$, where H_c is that from

column 3.

Table V The lower, H_c (0), and upper H_{cU} (0),

thermodynamic and lower, H_{c1} (0), and upper, H_{c2} (0)

critical magnetic fields of some high-T_c superconductors.

Parameter	Bi Sr Ca Cu$_2$ O$_{10}$	La$_{1.85}$ Sr$_{0.15}$ Cu O$_4$	La$_{1.85}$ Sr$_{0.15}$ Cu O$_4$	Y Ba$_2$ Cu$_3$ O
$T_c{}^a$ (K)	85	39	37	89-10
$\theta_D{}^a$ (K)	550	350-400	285-450	300-50
κ	209^b	68^b	62^c	45-150
H_c (0)^e (kOe)	7.98	2.71-3.31	2.04-4.05	10.1-29.1
H_{c1} (0) ^{f}(Oe)	144	119-145	96-191	174-239
$\frac{D}{M}$ N$_A$(10^{22} cm^{-3})	4.45	4.10	4.16	4.35, 4.37
H_{cU} (0)^g (T)	5.32	1.73-2.12	1.32-2.61	6.65-19.2
H_{c2} (0)^h (T)	1572	166-204	116-229	432-4073

[a] References 16, 23, and 28.

[b] This value of k $(=\lambda / \xi)$ was calculated assuming

$\lambda = 2000 \overset{\circ}{A}$ (reference 31).

The coherence length ξ was calculated using the corrected

BCS equation $\xi = 0.18$ ($\hbar$ v_F / k_B T_c), (reference 16).

[c] Reference 31.

d Reference 32.

e The thermodynamic critical field, H_c (0) is calculated

using the equation

$$H_c(0) = \left[\frac{24\,\pi^5}{5}\, n\,k_B\,T_c \left(\frac{T_c}{\theta_D} \right)^3 \right]^{1/2},$$

where $n \approx 1 \times 10^{21}$ cm^{-3}.

f The lower critical field, H_{c1} (0), was found using the

equation $H_{c1} \approx \dfrac{H_c}{\sqrt{2}\,\kappa}\, \ln \kappa.$

g The thermodynamic upper critical magnetic field at $T = 0$

is determined through the equation

$$H_{cU}(0) = \left[\frac{24\,\pi^5 D}{5\,M}\, N_A\,k_B\,T_c \left(\frac{T_c}{\theta_D} \right)^3 \right]^{1/2}.$$

h The upper critical field, H_{c2} (0) is found through

$H_{c2} \approx \sqrt{2}\,\kappa\,H_{cU}.$

Table **VI** The experimental and theoretical values of the jump in the electronic specific heat for some superconducting elements.

Element	η^a	$\delta\gamma / \gamma_n{}^a$	$\delta\gamma / \gamma_n{}^b$
Al	3.4	1.4	1.3
Cd	3.2	1.4	1.2
Hg	4.6	2.4	2.4
In	3.6	1.7	1.4
Nb	3.8	1.9	1.6
Pb	4.3	2.7	2.1
Sn	3.5	1.6	1.4
Ta	3.6	1.6	1.4
Tl	3.6	1.5	1.4
V	3.4	1.5	1.3
Zn	3.2	1.3	1.1

[a] Referemce 18.

[b] The theoretical values of the jump in the specific heat,

calculated from $\dfrac{\gamma_s - \gamma_n}{\gamma_n} = \dfrac{\eta^2}{9}$, where $\eta = \dfrac{2\Delta}{k_B\,T_c}$, and

2Δ is the magnitude of the energy gap.

GLOSSARY

A Particle's Lifetime: The time duration before the spontaneous decay of a particle to other particles.

Absolute Frame of Reference: An absolutely stationary (v=0) with reference frame.

Absolute Temperature (T): The temperature, T expressed in Kelvin*. In essence $T_K = T_C + 273.15$.

Active Site: *Enzymology.* the specific portion of an enzyme molecule that binds with or interacts with a substrate, forming an enzyme-substrate complex. Also, BINDING SITE, CATALYTIC SITE.

Acceleration: The velocity time rate of change.

Acceleration is a vector and is defined as $\vec{a} = \dfrac{\Delta \vec{v}}{\Delta t}$ where $\Delta \vec{v} = \vec{v}_f - \vec{v}_0$ is the change of velocity vector.

Acceptor of a Proton: Any negatively charged particle or electrode.

Acetylacholine (Ach): *Medicine.* adrenal cortical hormone.

Acid: *Chemistry.* **1.** any of a fundamental category of compounds whose water solutions are identified by certain common characteristics, such as a sour or biting taste, the ability to turn blue litmus paper red, and the ability to react with bases and certain metals to form salts. Other definitions identify substances as acids by their activities rather than by their properties, as follows: **a. (Arrhenius acid)** any substance that increases the concentration of hydrogen (H^+) ions when added to a water solution. The greater the increase, the stronger the acid. (S. A. Arrhenius, 1887) **b. (Bronsted** or **Bronsted-Lowry acid)** any substance that serves as a proton donor to another substance which accepts a proton. (J. N. Brønsted and T. M. Lowry, 1923) **c. (Lewis acid)** any substance that accepts a pair of electrons to form a covalent bond. (G. N. Lewis, about 1915).

Acinus: *plural,* **acini.** *Botany.* **1.** any of the small berries or drupelets making up a compound fruit in plants such as the blackberry. **2.** a berry that grows in clusters; e.g., a grape or current. *Anatomy.* **3.** a cluster of secretory cells that surround and empty into cavities **4.** any small, sac-like dilatation, especially one found in a gland. (A Latin word meaning "grape," so called because of its shape.)

Actin: *Biochemistry.* a protein that plays an important role in the contraction and relaxation of striated muscle.

Actin-Myosin (A-M) Complex: A reversible complex of actin and myosin.

Action potential: *Physiology.* a rapid change in the polarity of the membrane of a neuron, gland, or muscle fiber that facilitates the interaction and transmission of impulses. Also, SPIKE POTENTIAL. *Behavior.* see TENDENCY.

Activation Energy: The energy needed to activate a reaction.

Active Site: *Enzymology.* the specific portion of an enzyme molecule that binds with or interacts with a substrate, forming an enzyme-substrate complex. Also, BINDING SITE, CATALYTIC SITE.

Active Site of Enzymes The same as active site

Actomyosin: *Biochemistry.* a complex of the proteins actin and myosin that is found in muscle cells (myofibrils) and is responsible for muscle contraction.

Adenosine DiPhosphate (ADP): *Biochemistry.* $C_{10}H_{15}N_5O_{10}P_2$, a substance involved in energy metabolism; formed by the breakdown of adenosine triphosphate.

Adenosine TriPhosphate (ATP): *Biochemistry.* ATP, a nucleotide present in all living cells and acting as an energy source for many metabolic processes and required for ribonucleic acid synthesis.

Aerobic: *Biology.* **1.** requiring atmospheric oxygen to live. **2.** relating to or occurring in the presence of oxygen. *Bacteriology.* relating to or caused by aerobic bacteria. *Medicine.* requiring supplemental oxygen for respiration. *Physiology.* relating to or being a form of aerobic exercise. Thus, **aerobic walking, aerobic dancing,** and so on.

Aerobic Production of ATP: The path of ATP production using atmospheric oxygen.

Afferent: *Physiology.* moving or carrying inward or toward a central part. Thus, **afferent arteriole.** *Neurology.* **1.** a nerve that transmits sensory impulses toward the central nervous system

Affinity: a connection or relationship; specific uses include: *Biology.* a structural resemblance between species or higher groups, indicative of common ancestry. *Chemistry.* the force by which particles and substances are attracted to others and held together in compounds. *Immunology.* the measurement of the strength with which an antibody combining site binds with a single unit or determinant of an antigen. *Computer Programming*. see AFFINITY FACTOR.

AIDS: *Medicine*. Acquired Immuno Deficiency Syndrome, an epidemic retroviral disease due to infection with Human Immunodeficiency Virus (HIV-1), transmissible via blood or semen, and characterized by an ineffective immune response; the disease follows a protracted and debilitating course and has a poor prognosis. Those at risk include homosexual or bisexual males, intravenous drug abusers, hemophiliacs and other blood transfusion recipients, all sexual contacts of males in at-risk groups, and newborn infants of mothers with AIDS. (An acronym for the full name Acquired ImmunoDeficiency Syndrome.)

Algae: *Biology*. any of a large group of mostly aquatic organisms that contain chlorophyll and other pigments and can carry on photosynthesis, but lack true roots, stems, or leaves; they range from microscopic single cells to very large multicellular structures; included are nearly all seaweeds. (From Latin *alga,* "seaweed.")

Alpha (α) Particle: The nucleus of the Helium four, ^{4}He atom.

Alveolar Ducts: *Anatomy*. any of the small air passages in the lung connecting the respiratory bronchioles and the alveolar sacs.

Alveolar Sacs: *Anatomy*. a group of alveoli having a common opening.

Alveolar Type I Cells: 40% (120 Million) of total 300 Million alveolar cells.

Alveolar Type II Cells: 60% (180 Million) of total 300 million alveolar cells. They produce pulmona Surfactant.

Alveoli: the plural of ALVEOLUS

Alveolocapillary Membrance: The ultimate functional unit linking the pulmonary and cardiovascular systems.

Amino Acids: *Biochemistry.* any organic compound containing an amino (-NH$_2$) and a carboxyl (-COOH) group; there are 20 α-amino acids from which proteins are synthesized during ribosomal translation of mRNA. An **essential amino acid** is any one of the amino acids that are essential for metabolism, health, and growth, but that are not synthesized by the body and thus must be obtained from food. For humans, these include <u>isoleucine,</u> <u>leucine</u>, lysine, <u>methionine</u>, <u>phenylalanine</u>, <u>threonine</u>, <u>tryptophan, valine</u>, and (during growth periods) <u>arginine</u> and <u>histidine</u>. A **nonessential amino acid** is an amino acid that is synthesized by the body and thus not specifically required in the diet. These include alanine, asparagine, aspartic acid, cysteine, glutamine, glutamic acid, glycine, proline, serine, and tyrosine.

Amplifier: An electronic device which receives the electrical signals and strengthens them.

Anaerobic Glycolysis: Biochemistry. a process in which sugar is broken down into smaller molecules in the absence of oxygen; the conversion of glucose to lactic acid.

Anaerobic Biology: 1. occurring with little or no oxygen. 2. of or relating to anaerobes. Also, anaerobiotic, anerobic.

Anatomical: *Anatomy.* of or relating to anatomy.

Angstrom, A$^{\circ}$: A unit of length equal to 1×10^{-10} meter.

Antibiotic: *Biology.* **1.** having the ability to destroy life, or to interfere significantly with life processes. **2.** any substance or agent capable of having this effect.any substance or agent capable of having this effect. *Microbiology.* a chemical substance that is important in the treatment of infectious diseases, produced either by a microorganism or semisynthetically, having the capacity in dilute solutions to either kill or inhibit the growth of certain other harmful microorganisms. Antibiotics are widely used and include penicillin, streptomycin, and tetracycline.

Antibody: *Immunology.* A protein, produced as a result of the introduction of an antigen, that has the ability to combine with the antigen that caused its production. Also, IMMUNE BODY.

Antigen: Any substance that the body regards as foreign.

Antigen-Dependent Differentiation: The division of the B cell in the presence of an antigen.

Antiparticle: A twin of a particle whose everything (every physical parameter) is the same as, except for its electric charge which is opposite to, that of the particle.

Arrhenius' Equation: *Physical Chemistry.* a rate equation that is used for many chemical transformations and processes, in which the rate is exponentially related to temperature; one version is $k = Ae^{-Ea/RT}$, in which k is the rate constant of the chemical reaction, A is a constant called the preexponential factor or frequency factor, E_a is the activation energy, R is the gas constant, and T is the absolute temperature. (From S. A. Arrhenius.)

Arterial: *Anatomy.* of or relating to an artery or arteries.

Astronomical Unit (A.U.): The average earth-sun distance. It is approximately equal to 1.49597870×10^{8} km.

Atmospheric Pressure: *Physics.* the pressure of the earth's atmosphere. See ATMOSPHERE. *The force of the air on the unit area at the sea level. The atmospheric pressure is 1.013×10^{5} Pascal's. or 1.013×10^{5} Newton/m^{2}.*

Atomic Mass Unit, u: 1/12 of the mass of a carbon atom, $_{6}^{12}C$. In terms of this unit the mass of the electron, proton, and neutron are respectively 5.485799×10^{-4} u, 1.007276 u, and 1.008665 u.

ATP-ase: ATP – Syntase or the $F_0 F_1$ enzyme.

Avagadro's Number: The number of atoms, N_A in one atom gram of a substance or the number of molecules, N_A in one mole of a substance. In essence $N_A = 6.0221367 \times 10^{23}$ mol^{-1}.

Axolema: The extension of the soma cell membrane along the axon.

Axon: *Anatomy.* an extension of a neuron that carries propagated impulses.

Azimuthal Angle: ϕ The angle that the x-y plane component of the three dimensional position vector, $\vec{r}$ makes with the x axis.

B Lymphocytes: B Cells

Bacteria: A single cellular microorganism lacking the nuclear membrane. The size of the bacteria is about 1 mm. The function of the bacteria is mostly comprized of decaying the organic matter.

Base: *Chemistry.* any of a fundamental category of compounds that are identified by certain common characteristics, such as a bitter taste, a slippery feeling in water solution, the ability to turn litmus paper blue, and the ability to react with acids to form salts. Other definitions identify substances as bases by their activities rather than by their properties, as follows: a.also, Arrhenius base.any substance that increases the concentration of hydroxide (OH⁻) ions when added to a water solution. The greater the increase, the stronger the base. b. also, Brønstedor Brønsted-Lowry base. any substance that accepts a proton from another substance which serves as a proton donor. c. also, Lewis base. any substance that donates a pair of electrons to form a covalent bond. Biology. the part of a plant or organ that is nearest its point of attachment.

Bicarbonate: *Inorganic Chemistry.* a salt made by the neutralization of one hydrogen atom in carbonic acid; a salt containing the $-HCO_3$

Big Bang Theory: Theory of the birth of the Universe out of an initial explosion which started time and created the expanding space.

Bilirubin: *Biochemistry.* $C_{33}H_{36}N_4O_6$, a red-orange bile pigment formed from the bile pigment biliverdin and resulting from heme catabolism (mainly the breakdown of aged red blood cells); high concentrations lead to jaundice.

Binding Energy (w_B): The energy which is released when two objects adhere to each other such that in order to separate the objects from each other the binding energy, w_B must be given to the system (of the two objects).

Binding Site: see ACTIVE SITE.

Biochemist: the person concerned with all aspects of the chemistry of living organisms.

Bioengineering: *Biotechnology*. the science that specializes in the manufacture of artificial replacements for various parts or organs of the body. *Chemical Engineering*. the application of engineering methods for achieving biosynthesis of animal and plant products, such as fermentation processes. *Engineering*. any of various other applications of engineering methods and technology to the fields of medicine or biology.

Biophysicist: A physicist who applies physical laws to the biological systems.

Bioscientists: Any Scientist applying his science to biology.

Biosynthesis: *Biotechnology*. the science that specializes in the manufacture of artificial replacements for various parts or organs of the body. Chemical Engineering. the application of engineering methods for achieving biosynthesis of animal and plant products, such as fermentation processes. Engineering. any of various other applications of engineering methods and technology to the fields of medicine or biology.

Black Hole: A super-massive object ($m \approx 3$ times the mass of the sun) with a very small radius (often a few kilometers).

Blood Plasma: The blood without its cells. The blood liquid part containing ionized salts, proteins, vitamins, amino acids, glucose, and fat.

Bohr Radius: The closest radius of the electron (around the proton) in the hydrogen atom, $a = 5.29 \times 10^{-11}$ m.

Boltzman Constant: $K = 1.381 \times 10^{-23}$ J.K.$^{-1}$

Bombardment: Sending a shower of radiation to something.

Bond Strength: The measure of the binding energy w_B

Bone Marrow: *Histology.* soft, higly vascular connective tissue that occurs primarily in certain flat bones and serves as the main area of red and white blood cell production.

Breakdown of glucose: $C_6H_{12}O_6 + 6O_2 \rightarrow 6CO_2 + 6H_2O$

Bronchi: *Anatomy.* the plural of *bronchu,* part of a lung .

Bronchioles: the plural of bronchiole. Part of a lung.

Buffer: *Computer Technology.* an intermediate storage area used to compensate for differences in rates of data flow when information is being transmitted from one computer device to another. *Electricity.* a circuit or other component used to prevent undesirable electrical interaction between circuits or components. *Chemistry.* a solution containing a weak acid and a conjugate base of this acid (or, less commonly, a weak base and its conjugate acid); it resists change in its pH level when an acid or a base is added to it, because the acid neutralizes an added base and vice versa. Also, BUFFER SOLUTION. *Agronomy.* organic matter or a carbonate and phosphate compound in the soil that preserves hydrogen-ion concentrations and resists change in pH value. *Ecology.* see BUFFER SPECIES.

Ca^{2+}, Mg^{2+}, Na^+, K^+, Cl^-: Ionized atoms of Ca, Mg, Na, K, and Cl , i. e., atoms which have lost 2, 2, 1, 1, and gained 1 electron respectively.

Calorie: A unit of energy (especially thermal energy). One calorie is equal to 4.186 Joules.

Cancer: *Oncology.* a malignant tumor whose cells have the properties of endless replication, loss of contact inhibition, invasiveness and the ability to metastasize and whose result, generally, if left untreated, is fatal.

Capacitor: A combination of two electrically conducting plates on the surface of one of which we have an amount of positive electric charge, +Q and on the surface of the other we have an equal amount of negative charge, -Q.

Capillary: *Anatomy.* **1.** any of the tiny blood vessels through which exchange of materials between the blood and surrounding tissues takes place; serve to join the arteries with the veins. **2.** any tube having a very small bore. *Geology.* describing a mineral that forms hairlike or threadlike crystals.

Capillary Network: *Network of capillaries.*

Capture Model: Theory of the formation of the planets in other parts of the galaxy thereafter being captured by the gravitational attraction of the sun.

Carbohydrate Breakdown: The decomposition of hydrocarbons to Co_2 and H_2

Carbon (C): *Chemistry.* a very common nonmetallic element having the symbol C, the atomic number 6, an atomic weight of 12.01115, and melting point about 3600°C; found in the crystalline forms of diamond and graphite and in various amorphous forms including charcoal, coal, and coke; the defining element of organic compounds, and the active element of photosynthesis. The natural, dominant isotope of carbon, *carbon-12,* is the basis of the atomic weights of other elements (^{12}C = at. wt. 12). (From the Latin word for "coal" or "charcoal.")

Carbon Dioxide: *Inorganic Chemistry.* CO_2, a colorless, odorless, noncombustible gas that is slightly more than 1.5 times as dense as air; becomes a solid (dry ice) below -78.5°C. It is present in the atmosphere as a result of the decay of organic material and the respiration of living organisms, and it represents about 0.033% of the air. Carbon dioxide is produced by the burning of wood, coal, coke, oil, natural gas, or other fuels containing carbon, by the action of an acid on a carbonate, or naturally from springs and wells. It has a wide range of uses, as in carbonated beverages, fire extinguishers, refrigeration systems, and aerosols.

Cardiac: Relating to the heart

Cardiovascular: Anatomy. of or relating to the heart and blood vessels.

Catalyze: *Chemistry.* to change or bring about by catalysis.

Catalyzed Fusion: A fusion which is led to take place at much lower temperatures than those at the core of the sun (millions of degrees).

Catastrophe Model: A theory of the sudden separation of the planets from the sun due to its collision with meteorites.

Cause and Effect: Emerged out of the principle of causality stating that any manifestation is the effect of a cause. In fact the cause is like the raw material and the effect is like the product of a process.

Cell Differentiation: *Cell Biology*. the process by which a cell becomes specialized for a specific structure or function by selective gene expression of some genes and selective repression of others.

Cell Division: *Cell Biology*. the process by which two cells are produced from a single cell, including both nuclear division and cytoplasmic division.

Cell Membrane: *Cell Biology*. a protein-containing lipid bilayer that surrounds a cell, defining the interface between the cell and its environment and providing a semi permeable barrier to the entry of molecules into the cell.

Cell Membrane Electric Potential Difference: (EPD) The potential difference

Cell Proliferation: Cell division between the cell inner and outer membranes (about 60 mW with the inner layer being nega.

Cell: The basic and pragmatic unit of most organic Structures able to live as an independent unit.

Cellular Cycle: The cellular life cycle.

Central Nervous System: (CNS) *Anatomy.* the brain and spinal cord.

Cerebellum: *Anatomy.* the section of the brain behind and below the cerebrum, consisting of two lateral lobes and a middle lobe that function as a coordinating center for muscle movement.

Chain Reactions: Reactions in which one particle gets into and two of the same kind emerge.

Chemical Reaction: An interaction among atoms and/or molecules where electrons are exchanged.

Chemical Structure: The atomic map of a compound.

Chemical Transducer: A chemical compound used in converting one form of energy to another.

Chemiosmotic Theory: The most widely accepted theory of the synthesis of Adenosine TriPhosphate (ATP) through the protonation of Adenosine DiPhosphate (ADP) and an inorganic Phosphorous (P_i).

Choloroplast: A chlorophyl-containing organelle found in an organism cells undergoing through photosynthesis.

Citrates: Compound of citric acid and a base. Citrus fruits carry Citric acid, $C_6H_8O_7$ [$HO_2C_2H_2C$ (OH)(CO$_2$H) CH$_2$CO$_2$H].

Classical Mechanics: The study of the lows of motion of macroscopic objects.

Cluster: *Astronomy*; a group op seemingly closer objects (e.g., galaxies).

Cohesive Energy: The energy needed to disassemble it to its elemental parts. In essence the cohesive energy is the same as the binding energy of the system.

Cold Fusion: The adhesion of atomic nuclei at relatively lower temperatures (than, e.g., those at the core of the sun), e.g. T | 1000 K.

Cold Fusion: The same as catalyzed fusion*.

Collagen Fibers: A fibrous protein found in connective tissue including skin, bone, ligaments, and cartilage.

Colonal Selection Theory: A theory on the mechanism of the body immune system

Complete Oscillation: A wave which contains both positive and negative part of the vibrations (usually of the $\vec{E}$ and $\vec{B}$ fields).

Complex Numbers: Numbers which are multiples of a real number with. $\sqrt{-1}$

Composition: *Chemistry*. **1.** the elements or compounds of which a substance is composed.

Concentration of X ([X]):   The quantity of dissolved substance per unit (one mole) of solvent in a solution.

Conductance, g: The reverse of resistance, R.   The resistance of a wire, R is the measure of how much electric power, P is converted to heat (thermal energy) once there is an electric current, I flowing through that wire.

Conductivity: The ability of a substance or medium to direct heat, sound, light, and electric current.

Conservation Of Momentum and Energy: A fundamental principle of physics, stating: the total momentum (or energy) of an isolated (not interacting with its outside) system remains constant during all (or any) internal interaction.

Contraction: The one, two, or three dimensional decrease of a substance due to stress or thermal effects.

Conversion of Mass to Energy: Naturally transpiring in the fusion of nuclei lighter than iron, Fe and the fission of nuclei heavier than iron.

Core (of the Earth):   Made of two parts the liquid outer core and the solid inner core. The core density varies from 9 gm/cm^3 to 13 gm/cm^3. The core is believed to be made of iron, Fe and nickel, Ni.

Core of the Sun: The inner part (of the sun) with a radius of one quarter of that of the sun, $R_{Core} = (1/4)R_{Sun}$ ($R_{Sun} = 682,265$ km). At the core of the sun the density is r = 158 gm/cm^3, the temperature is $T = 1.5X10^7$ K.

Cosmic Journey: The (billions of light years) journey trip through space.

Cosmic Ray: The particles (mainly protons, the nuclei of the lighter atoms up to iron, and photons) arriving at the Earth's atmosphere from the outer space galaxies, subsequently breaking to other particles (π and μ mesons and photons).

Coulomb's Law of Electrostatic Force: A law identifying the repulsive and/or attractive electric force among the like and/or dislike electric charges. According to this law the force, F between two charges is proportional with the magnitudes of charge Q_1, charges Q_2, and the inverse of their center to center distance squared, r^2. The proportionality constant is called the electrostatic constant,

$K (= 9.0 \times 10^9 Nm^2/C^2)$. In essence $F = \dfrac{kQ_1 Q_2}{r^2}$. The

force, F is along the line joining the center of the charges.

Crbohydrate: An organic compound of Carbon and Hydrogen with a general chemical formula of $C_n(H_2O)_m$

Creatine Phosphate (CrP): A compound, synthesized from amino acids arginine, glycine and metheonine.

Crust: The relatively thinner outer layer of the Earth.

Crystallization: The entrapment of the atoms or molecules of a substance (mostly liquids during their solidification) at the corners of geometrical patterns which by repeating fill the three dimensional space, e.g., simple, body centered, and face centered cubic crystals.

Curvature of Space: The bending of the space around a very massive object.

Cytochrome (a, a3, b, c1) : (A protein with an iron which can accept or donate an electron: embedded the inner mitochondrion membrane).

Dalton: A usualy used unit of molecular mass equal to 1/12 times the mass of carbon approximately equal to 1.657×10^{-27} kg.

Damping: The spatial or temporal diminishing of a wave due to the conversion of the wave to other energy shapes.

D-D Fusion: The fusion of two deuterium nuclei. A deuterium nucleus is a hydrogen nucleus with an additional neutron.

Dead Space: *Anatomy.* the volume of the air passages from the nose down to the level where oxygen and carbon dioxide are interchanged. Also, **anatomical dead space.** *Physiology.* an area of the alveoli where very little gas is being exchanged. Also, **physiological dead space.** *Surgery.* the empty cavity that is left following the closure of a surgical incision or a wound, permitting the accumulation of blood or serum and resulting in a delay in healing. *Thermodynamics.* a space whose volume is occupied by a gas with a different temperature from that of the main body.

Decomposition: *Chemistry.* a process in which one or more substances break down into simpler molecular substances, as from the effects of heat, light, chemical or biological activity, and   so   on. *Geochemistry.*   see   CHEMICAL WEATHERING.

Dendrite: *Neurology.* a branchlike extension of the cytoplasm of a neuron; composing most of the neuron's receptive surface, dendrites resemble axons in structure but generally extend into treelike processes, especially in multipolar neurons. Also, DENDRON.

Density: $\rho = \dfrac{m}{v}$ The mass of the unit volume of a substance. The density of an object is defined as its mass divided by its volume.

Depolarization: *Electricity.* **1.** the removal, decrease, or prevention of agents that cause polarization in an electric cell. **2.** the addition of substances to depolarize a cell. *Optics.* a process in which a beam of polarized light is reflected in all directions perpendicular to its axis so that its vibrations no long occur along a single plane.

Deposition of Protons: The displacement of the protons (often against the repulsive force of the other protons) from one place to the other

Detecting Devices: A device used to detect the passage of particles through their interaction with the particles inside.

Deuterium (D) :   An isotope of the hydrogen atom. A hydrogen atom with an extra neutron in its nucleus. Therefore a Deuterium nucleus contains a proton and a neutron.

Differential Equation: Equations which only identify the local (pointwise) behavior of the functions.

Diffusion: The penetration of a substance through another one.

Disease: *Medicine.* **1.** any abnormal condition of body functions or structure that is considered to be harmful to the affected individual; an illness or disorder. **2.** a specific illness or disorder that is identified by a characteristic set of signs and symptoms, caused by such factors as infection, toxicity, genetic or developmental defects, dietary deficiency or imbalance, or environmental effects.

Distribution of Energy: The spatial functional form of the energy.

DNA Molecules: *Molecular Biology.* the double helix structure of DNA, as identified by Watson and Crick, consisting of two strands of DNA wound together, usually with a right-hand twist.

Donor of a Proton: A compound which give a nucleus of the H atom (H^+).

Dopler (Red) Shift: A shift in the wavelength, of light (toward that of red) due to the receding speed of the light source.

Dosage: *Medicine.* the giving of medicine or any other therapeutic agent in prescribed amounts for a particular patient or condition. *Genetics.* see GENE DOSAGE. *Nucleonics.* see DOSE

Drift Velocity of Charges: The velocity of the electrons (or holes) in a particular direction in electrical conductors.

Dynamic Variables: Those variables such as momentum, angular momentum, potential and kinetic energies, and etc. which identify the mechanical state of a system.

Dyspnea: *Medicine.* difficult or labored breathing, usually associated with serious disease of the heart or lungs. Thus, **dyspneic.**

$e^2/2r$: The self energy of a particle with an electric charge of $\pm e$.

Effector Cell: *Cell Biology.* a cell that acts in response to a certain stimulus or is capable of mediating a function.

Efferent: *Physiology.* **1.** referring to a neuron that carries motor impulses away from the central nervous system. **2.** of or relating to a blood vessel through which blood flows away from the heart.

Elastic Collision: A collision in which the colliding objects touch each other for a very short time only. A good example is the collision between two billiard balls.

Elastic Deformation: A returning to its original shape deformation of the atoms from their equilibrium (normal) sites in a solid.

Electric Charge Plasma: An   ensemble   (a   lot   of particles) of ionized atoms where the electrons have left the bond of the nuclei and have at least enough kinetic energy so they cannot be captured by the nuclei. In essence, a mixture of the negative and positive charges where the charges' kinetic energy prevents them of binding with each other.

Electric Conduction: A process in which the electrons enter from one side (often of a wire) and exit its other end.

Electric Field: $\vec{E}$ The vector of the electric force on a unit charge (+1 Coulomb) at different points of space.

Electrical Conductor: A substance which conducts the flow of the electrons through itself.

Electrical Impulse: A sudden flow of electrical energy into or out of a system.

Electrical Potential Energy: The (electrostatic) energy needed to bring (and hold stationary) a charge, Q in the vicinity of other charges.

Electrical Signal: any change in the electromagnetic field.

Electrical Stimuli: Disturbance in the electric and / or magnetic fields.

Electromagnetic (E&M):   Of electric and magnetic nature like electromagnetic waves.

Electron Volt (eV):   A unit of energy (especially electrical energy). One electron volt, eV is equal to 1.6×10^{-19} joules*.

Electron: An elementary particle of mass 9.11×10^{-31} kg, electric charge of 1.6×10^{-19} Coulomb, and spin 1/2 or -1/2,

Electronic Transport: The apparent transportation of the electrons through matter during, e.g., electrical or thermal conduction.

Electrostatic: That part of electricity wherein the charges are (or can be treated as) stationary.

Electrostatic Constant: The constant in the Coulomb's equation to find the magnitude of the electrostatic force between two electric charges. In essence, the electrostatic constant is the "k" in $F = \dfrac{kQ_1 Q_2}{r^2}$. The magnitude of k is $k = 8.99 \times 10^9$ N.m^2/C^2.

Elementary Particles: Those subatomic particles such as electron, proton, neutron, π and μ mesons.

Embryonic Cell: Cells in their division state.

Energy: The ability to do mechanical work.

Ensemble: An assembly of a very large number of systems (usually similar to one another).

Entropy: An indication of the number of possible states accessible to a system. Since the number of accessible states to a system is also proportional to the amount of heat, Q flowing into the system at any temperature, T the entropy, S is then proportional to the thermal energy, Q given to the system. In essence $S = \dfrac{Q}{T}$.

Enzyme Inhibition: The adaptive decrease in the number of enzyme molecules.

Enzyme: A (protein structured molecule) catalyst of biological chemical interactions.

Epithelial: *Histology.* of, relating to, or composed of epithelium or epithelial cells.

Epithelium: *Histology.* an animal tissue composed of cells that are packed tightly together, with little intercellular matrix; it covers the external surface of the body and also internal surfaces such as the lining of tracts and vessels.

Erythrocyte: *Hematology.* the major cellular element of the peripheral blood, containing hemoglobin and specialized to carry oxygen. In humans, the mature form is normally a nonnucleated, yellowish, biconcave disk that is adapted to carry oxygen by virture of its configuration and hemoglobin content. Also, RED BLOOD CELL, CORPUSCLE.

Ether, or Etheric Fluid: The medium conducting (the propagation of) light through itself.

Eukaryotes: A cellular organism with a nucleus containing genetic codes. Every cellular organism except bacteria.

Excitable Cell: A nerve and /or muscle cell.

Exocytosis: *Cell Biology.* a process by which a variety of secretory products are released from the cell via transport within vesicles to the cell surface and subsequent fusion with the plasma membrane, resulting in the extrusion of the vesicle contents from the cell.

Expansion of the Universe: The departure of the stars from the Earth identified through their light wavelength, λ spectrum leaning towards that of the red, called the Doppler red shift.

Expansion: The one, two, or three dimensional increase of a substance due to stress or thermal effects.

Experimental: The (repeatable) laboratory observations.

Expiration: *Physiology.* **1.** see EXHALATION. **2.** another term for death.

F_0 (Fraction Zero) Enzyme: The protein structures at the stem of the knoblike spheres elevated from the inner mitochondrion membrane. The F_0 enzyme is part of the protons' pathway back to the mitochondria matrix.

F_0-F_1 Enzyme: An enzyme called ATP-syntase or ATP-ase. The site of ATP synthesis in mitochondrion. The actual pathway of protons whose transfer of kinetic energy result in ATP synthesis .

F₁ (Fraction One) Enzyme: A knoblike protein sphere connected to the inner mitochondrial membrane which is the site of the ATP generation through conduction of the protons back to the inside of the mitochondrion matrix.

Faraday's Law of Induction: A law which expresses that the time variation of magnetic flux , $\varphi = \vec{B} \cdot \vec{A}$ produces an electric potential difference, V (ξ) (or electric power, P).

Fast Protons: Protons with energies, $W \geq$ a few GeV.

Fast Twitch unit: A type of a motor neuron with slow oxidative metabolism.

Fat: *Anatomy.* adipose tissue composed of cells containing glycerol and fatty acid; white or yellowish tissue that forms soft pads between various organs of the body, serves to smooth and round out bodily contours, and furnishes a reserve supply of energy. *Biochemistry.* one of a group of glycerides of higher fatty acids, such as palmitic acid, stearic acid, and oleic acid, that is an essential component of the human diet.

Fat Breakdown: The decomposition of fat molecules.

Fatigue: *Physiology.* **1.** a state of increased discomfort and decreased efficiency resulting from prolonged or excessive exertion. **2.** the loss of power or of the capacity to respond to stimulation, as in a muscle that is exercised until it loses its ability to contract. *Psychology.* see BATTLE FATIGUE; BEHAVIORAL FATIGUE.

Fermentation: *Microbiology.* the chemical decomposition of a substance, especially a carbohydrate, brought about by enzymes, bacteria, yeasts, or molds, generally in the absence of oxygen. *Biotechnology.* the process of culturing cells or other microorganisms in a container, bioreactor, or fermenter for experimental or commercial purposes.

Fiber: *Materials.* a thin, threadlike piece of any material. *Nutrition.* **1.** the structural part of plants and plant products consisting of carbohydrates that, when eaten, stimulate peristalsis in the intestine the structural **2.** food, such as whole grains, fruits, and vegetables, that contains large amounts of such carbohydrates *Botany.* a thick-walled, narrow, elongated sclerenchyma cell, often lignified, that tapers at both ends.

Fictitious Forces: Forces which are not really there but the problem will solve much more easily if we assume they are there.

Field: The propulsion a substance exerts on the objects around itself. The field of a substance is the force (vector) on the unit item of the kind of desired field. For example the gravitational field of a mass M kg at any point r, is its gravitational force (vector) on a 1 kg mass at that point.

Fine Structure Constant: A constant which is equal to $e^2/\hbar c$.

Fission: Splitting of, especially and usually the nucleus of an atom heavier than iron, Fe.

Fitting Factors: Factors which fit the theoretical results to the experimental ones.

Flavin MonoNucleotide:(FMN) *Biochemistry.* $C_{17}H_{21}N_4O_9P$, a phosphoric ester of riboflavin that constitutes the coenzyme of various flavoproteins.

Flux (φ) of a Vector, $\vec{A}$:   The (vector) addition (integral) of all vectors, $\vec{A}$ over a surface, S.

Force: The negative of the spatial, (x in one dimension) energy, W rate of change. In essence in one dimension

$$F = -\frac{dW}{dx}.$$

Free Particles: Particles not interacting with any field.

Frequency, f: The number of oscillations in one second.

Fungus: *plural,* **fungi** *Mycology.* an organism possessing cells with nuclei and rigid cell walls and lacking chlorophyll.

Furrier Analysis: Building a function, f with sine and cosine waves as the construction units (bricks).

Fusion Energy: The energy gained through the union of separated atomic nuclei

Galactic Space: The space between galaxies.

Galaxy: An assembly of billions of solar systems.

Gastrointestinal: The stomach and the intestinal related functions.

Gas Constant : R = 8.314 J/Mol.K

General Relativity: A set of rules (and equations) connecting the measurements of observers in different fields (of forces) with respect to one another and to the occurring event. Albert Einstein's theory which replaces energy fields with the curvature (the metric) of space.

Gibbs Free Energy: The Gibbs free energy, G of a system is defined as $G = E - TS + pV$ where E is the internal energy T is the absolute temperature, S is the entropy, p is the pressure, and V is the volume of the system.

Giga: (G) A manifold of a substance equal to an aggregation of 1×10^9 parts.

Gland Cell: *Anatomy.* Any one of the various organs composed of specialized cells that secrete or excrete a material that is not related to ordinary metabolism, such as the pituitary gland, which produces hormones, and the spleen, which takes part in blood production. *Botany.* A secreting structure or organ. *Engineering.* An apparatus that prevents leakage at the point at which a shaft emerges from a vessel containing a fluid under pressure. (Going back to the Latin word for "acorn.")

Glucose ($C_6H_{12}O_6$):   *Biochemistry.* $C_6H_{12}O_6$, a six-carbon aldose that is the major sugar in the blood and a key intermediate in metabolism; used as a fluid and nutrient replenisher, usually given intravenously. Also, DEXTROSE, CERELOSE, D-GLUCOPYRANOSE.

Glucose-6-Phosphate: *Biochemistry.* $C_6H_{13}O_9P$, a key intermediate formed in the biochemical interactions of gluconeogenesis or carbohydrate metabolism.

Glycogen: *Biochemistry.* $(C_6H_{10}O_5)_n$, a highly branched polysaccharide serving as a short-term storage substance, and, as such, subject to continuous synthesis and degradation.

Glycolitic Enzyme: An enzyme that catalyzes the hydrolysis of sugar.

Glycolitic Pathway: The oxygen absent pathway of one molecule of glucose transmutation to pyrovate and eventually synthesis of two ATP molecules.

Gradient: the rate of change of any physical quantity with respect to distance, as it progresses toward a maximum quantity.

Gram: (gm) $1X10^{-3}$ kg.

Gramicidin: One of the antibiotics produced by hacillus brevis.

Gravitation: The weakest force, F_G among the forces of nature known to man. The gravitational force between two objects is proportional to masses M_1, M_2, and to the inverse of their center to center distance squared, r^2. The constant of proportionality is called the universal gravitational constant,

G. in essence $F_G = -\dfrac{GM_1M_2}{r^2}$. The force, F_G is an attractive one along the line joining the two centers of masses. Gravity has appreciable magnitudes only when the masses involved are of celestial size.

Gravity: The attraction between two masses. Gravity is most visible among the astronomical objects.

Ground State: The state of least energy.

Group Velocity: (v_g) The measure of the spatial advancement of a wave, as a package.

H^+ Nucleus (Proton): An ionized hydrogen atom. A hydrogen atom which has lost its only electron. In essence a single proton.

Hard Component of Cosmic Ray: The high energy part of the cosmic ray. It can penetrate beyond 10 cm of lead.

Helium: (He) An atom with two electrons, two protons, and one or two neutrons.

Helium 3 and 4; ^{3}He and ^{4}He: Atoms with two electrons orbiting two central protons with respectively one and two neutrons (at their nuclei).

Hemapoietic Stem Cells: Blood forming stem cells.

Heme: *Biochemistry*. $C_{34}H_{32}O_4N_4Fe$, a protoheme or iron-porphyrin complex that has a protoporphyrin nucleus, specifically one containing the oxygen-binding portion of the hemoglobin molecule

Hemoglobin: Hematology. the oxygen-carrying pigment of the erythrocytes, formed by the developing erythrocyte in bone marrow. It is a complex protein composed of four heme groups and four globin polypeptide chains. They are designated α(alpha), β(beta), γ(gamma), and δ(delta) in an adult, and each is composed of several hundred amino acids.

Hepatocyte: *Histology*. the primary functional cell of the liver.
Hetrotrophic: Concerning something of different type than that which is being discussed..

High Energy Portion of the Cosmic Radiation: That part of the cosmic radiation whose particles have kinetic energies of the order 1-100 GeV.

Hydrogen Bond: Crystalline bonds that are relatively very strong, i.e., comparable to the ionization energy of the electron in hydrogen atom, (W = 13.6 eV).

Hydrogen Compounds: Those compounds which carry a hydrogen ion (a proton). Mostly Hydro-Carbons which are among organic compounds.

Hydrolysis: Capturing a Hydrogen atom or Ion.

Hydronium: (Hy) H_3O^+

Hydroquinone: (QH_2) *Organic Chemistry.* $C_6H_4(OH)_2$, combustible white crystals; soluble in water, alcohol, and ether, melts at 170°C and boils at 285°C; used in photography, medicine, paints, and motor oils.

Hyperpnea: Medicine. an abnormal increase in the depth and rate of breathing.

Ignition: To initiate the reaction.

Immunoglobins: (Ig) A family of proteins capable of acting as antibodies.

Immunological: The result of the study of immunity to disease.

Inductor: A coil of electric wire.

Inelastic Collision: A type of collision in which the colliding objects adhere (to each other) and conform one object (after collision).

Inertial Frames: Reference frames which move with constant velocity, $\vec{v}$ with respect to each other.

Ingestion: *Biology.* **1.** the action of taking food material; into gastro intestinal tract feeding; **2.** consumption. The process of food taking by a cell.

Injection of Light: Giving an acceleration to the object by exerting a force on it.

Injury: *Medicine.* Any damage or wound to the body; usually applied to damage inflicted by an external force.

Innervate: To stimulate the nerve supply of an organ.

Inorganic: *Biology.* **1.** not organic; not having the structure or undergoing processes that are characteristic of living organisms, i.e., plants and animals. **2.** not composed of living or formerly living material. *Chemistry.* **1.** not an organic substance; not a hydrocarbon or a derivative of hydrocarbon.not an organic substance; **2.** of or relating to inorganic chemistry.

Inorganic Phosphorus: Single phosphorous or that in minerals and salts.

Inspiration: *Physiology.* the act of drawing air from the outside of the body into the lungs.

Inspiration-Expiration of a Macroscopic Object: The expansion and contraction of an object due to that of its constituent particles.

Inspiration-Expiration of a Microscopic Particle: The increase and decrease in the peneration radius, r_0 of a particle.

Inspiration-Expiration of the Universe: The expansion and contraction of the whole universe.

Insulator: A substance which does not (or very hardly does) allow the passage of electrical current (electrons) through itself.

Internal Energy: The internal energy, E of a system is equal to the difference between the thermal energy, Q given to the system and the work, W done by the system.

In essence: $E = Q - W$.

Interstitium: The very small space between the cells.

Ion Channel: *Biochemistry*. a transmembrane pore that presents a hydrophilic channel for ions to cross a lipid bilayer down their electrochemical gradients.

Ion Current: A flow of the electric ions (e.g., Na^+, Ca^{2+}, K^+, Mg^{2+}, Cl^-) instead of the electrons for normal electrical conduction, e.g., in wires.

Ionic Bond: The bond between ions as impenetrable electrically charged spheres. The bond exists because of the electrostatic attraction-repulsion among the charged ions.

Ionic Current: The flow of the ions instead of the electrons (i.e., the electrical current).

Ionization Chamber: A device recording the passage or stopping of a particle.

Ionize: Giving an orbiting electron (negatively charged) enough energy to leave the bound of the nucleus. This (energy) is called the ionization energy.

Isotopes: Atoms with the same number of electrons and protons, Z but different number of neutrons, A-Z.

Joule: A unit of energy (especially mechanical energy). One Joule is equal to one kilogram.meter^2/s^2.

Kcal: Kilo-calories.

Kcal/mol: Kilo-calories per mole.

Kelvin: (K) A unit of temperature. One Kelvin is equal to one degree Centigrade. The only difference between Kelvin and Centigrade is in the definition of their zeros or starting points. The connecting equation is $T_K = T_C + 273.15$.

Kilo: (k) A manifold of a substance equal to an aggregation of 1×10^3 parts.

Kinetic Energy: That part of the system's energy which is proportional to the square of the speed and the mass of the system. In essence $KE = \frac{1}{2}Mv^2$

Lactic Acid: *Biochemistry.* $C_3H_6O_3$, the hydroxy acid that is formed from pyruvic acid when glycolysis proceeds under anaerobic conditions.

Laser: Light amplification by the stimulated emission of radiation.

Latent Heat: The thermal energy needed to change the state of a substance from solid to liquid with the temperature staying constant or from liquid to vapor and vice versa.
Length Contraction: The apparent decrease in the length of a relatively moving object. In essence $L = L_0 \sqrt{1 - \frac{v^2}{c^2}}$.

Leukocyte: Histology. a white or colorless cell of the blood, having a nucleus and either granular or non-granular cytoplasm; leukocytes function as bacterial or viral phagocytes, as detoxifiers of toxic proteins, and in the development of immunities. Also, WHITE BLOOD CELL.

Ligament: *Histology.* a type of white fibrous connective tissue that surrounds and holds bones together at joints. *Engineering.* the solid material piece of a tube sheet between adjacent holes. (Going back to a Latin word meaning "to tie.")

Linear Momentum $\vec{P} = m\vec{v}$:   The product of the particle mass times its velocity vector. In essence.

Lobar Bronchi: a defined separated apart of bronchi.

Lymph Node: *Anatomy.* one of the many rounded to oval masses of lymphatic tissue distributed along the lymphatic vessels that filter lymph. Also, **lymph gland.**

Lymphatic System: *Anatomy.* the system of lymphatic vessels, lymph nodes, and masses of lymphatic tissue, such as the spleen, that collects lymphatic fluid from the tissues, filters it, and returns it to the venous system; also transports fats and proteins to the blood system and restores to the circulation more than half of the fluid that filters out of the capillaries during normal exchange across capillary walls.

Lysosome: *Cell Biology.* an organelle containing hydrolytic enzymes that degrade macromolecules and other materials taken up by a cell during endocytosis.

M, $\vec{V}$, $\vec{P}$, KE, PE: Mass, velocity, momentum, kinetic energy, and potential energy.

Macrophages: A monocyte that has left circulation, settled, and matured in a tissue.

Magnet: A piece of an element which exhibits permanent magnetism.

Magnetic Field, $\vec{B}$:   The vector of the biggest (magnitude) magnetic force on a unit length (one meter) of a wire carrying one ampere of electric current, I at different points of space.

Mammalian: *Vertebrate Zoology.* **1.** an organism of the class Mammalia; a mammal. **2.** of or relating to this class.

Mantle: The thick solid layer between the crust* (the upper layer) and the core* (the central part) of the Earth.

Mass: (M) The content of the matter (or energy$/c^2$) of an object. The mass of an object is proportional to the number of the atoms (or molecules) present in it.

Mass Increase: The apparent relativistic increase in the mass of a relatively moving object.   In essence M=

$$m_0 \sqrt{1 \cdot \frac{v^2}{c^2}} \,.$$

Matching of Half Oscillations: The junction of the same wavelength, λ of pits and hills of a vibration.

Matter Part: That part of the substance which is equal to its total energy content divided by the square of the speed of light. In essence $m = \dfrac{E}{c^2}$

Maturation: Biology. 1. the process of coming to full development. 2. specifically, the final series of changes in the growth and formation of germ cells.

Mechanism: The physical procedures of transpiring.

Mega: (M) A manifold of a substance equal to an aggregation of 1×10^6 parts.

Melting Point: The temperature, T at which the substance melts.

Membrane Potential: Cell Biology. a difference in electrical potential that is obseved between the two sides of a cell membrane

Metabolism: All chemical reactions transpiring in organic structures.

Metabolize: Physiology. to change by metabolism.

Meteorite: Rocks that have arrived to the surface of the earth from distant parts of the solar system.

Micro, μ: A fraction of a substance equal to 1×10^{-6} part.

Microscopic: Of a size so small that unrecognizable with naked eye.

Mili: (m) a fraction of a substance equal to 1×10^{-3} part.

Mitochondrion: A small (0.7-1 micrometer) sausage or oval shape organism within the cytoplasm of the cell. It is the site of cell's aerobic (O_2 involved) respiration.

Mole: An aggregate of 6.0221367×10^{23} (Avagadro's number) molecules of a substance.

Molecular Oxygen: A system of two bound oxygen atoms (O_2).

Momentum: Defined as the product of mass and velocity, i.e., $\vec{P} = m\vec{v}$

Monochromatic Wave: A wave with only one wavelength, λ present and not a band of wavelengths.   In nature this wave cannot be identified.

Motor Neuron: *Physiology.* a neuron possessing a motor function; an efferent neuron conveying motor impulses in a pyramidal pathway, whose cell bodies are located in the nuclei of cranial nerves and in the anterior columns of gray matter of the spinal cord. Also, MOTONEURON.

Motor Unit: Anatomy. one motor neuron and the muscle fibers with which it synapses.

Moving Mass: The apparent mass of a moving (relatively fast) particle.

Mumolecule: Two muonic atoms which have made a bond.

Muon-Assisted Fusion: Cold fusion or the muon catalyzed fusion.

Muonic Atoms: An atom in which muon particles have occupied the electrons' place, orbiting the central nucleus.

Muonic Deuterium: (MD) A deuterium atom in which a muon particle has occupied the electron's place, orbiting the central proton and neutron.

Muscle Cell: Diameter of 10-100 mm and a length of 20 cm.

Myelin Sheath: Multiple concentric layers of shwann cells enveloping the axon acting as an insulation for the axon against the ion currents.

Myofibril: Composing the muscle fiber by an aggregation of hundreds. A myofibril is subdivided into sacromeres , has an average length of 2,25 mm.

Myoglobin: *Biochemistry.* an oxygen-transporting and storing pigment in muscle cells; it contains a heme (iron porphyrin) where oxygen binds. Also, **myohemoglobin.**

Myosin: Biochemistry. a globin that is the most abundant protein in muscle, occurring primarily in the A band, and forming the main constituent of the thick filaments of muscle fibers.

NAD$^+$: *Enzymology.* the oxidized form of nicotinamide adenine dinucleotide.

NADH: *Enzymology.* the reduced (hydrogen ion-carrying) form of nicotinamide adenine dinucleotide

Nano: (n) A fraction of a substance equal to 1×10^{-9} part.

Nano Meter: A tiny fraction of a meter, nm is equal to 1×10^{-9} meter.

Natural Logarithm: (ln) Generally the number 2^x means that we have to multiply the number 2 by itself x times. For example for x = 4 we have $2^4 = 2 \times 2 \times 2 \times 2 = 16$. The factor "x" is called the exponent of 2. On the other hand if for any number (positive and real), y we find that exponent (of 2) which satisfies the equation $2^x = y$ then x is called the natural logarithm, ln of y, therefore lny = x. For example the natural logarithm of number 16, ln16 is the number 4 because $2^4 = 16$ therefore we can write ln16 = 4.

Negative and Positive Half oscillation: The pits and hills of a vibration.

Nerve Cell: Cell Biology. a cell of the nervous system; a neuron

Neuromuscular Junction: *Anatomy*. the area where synapse occurs between a motor nerve fiber and the striated muscle fiber that it innervates; the expansion of the terminal branch of the axon forms the motor end plate and the opposed region of the surface of the muscle fiber forms the postsynaptic region.

Neuron: *Cell Biology*. one of the two principal types of nerve cells in the nervous system, usually consisting of a cell body, an axon, several dendrites, and specialized axon terminals, that is able to receive and conduct electrical impulses. Also, NEUROCYTE, NERVE CELL.

Neurotransmission: The transmission of substances like dopamine and alike.

Neuro-Transmitter: Substance which is released when the axon terminal is excited, of the presynaptic neuron

Neutrino, v: An elementary particle whose rest energy has been estimated $mc^2 \leq 35$ MeV.

Neutron Counting: Counting of the average number of produced neutrons in a reaction.   In essence, in fusion reactions. For each Watt of produced power this average is 1.42×10^{12}.

Neutron Star: A dying star with a mass about that of the sun with its electrons having collapsed in its nuclei thereby being made of all neutrons. Typical mass, diameter, density, and temperature of a neutron star are receptively 1.5 solar mass, 20 km, 1×10^{15} gm/cm^3, and 1×10^7 C^o.

Neutron: An electrically neutral elementary particle which (if is free) in about 15 minutes disintegrates to a proton, an electron, and another elementary particle called neutrino (v).

Newtonian Gravitation: The attracting force between two (usually heavenly) masses not too much bigger than the sun. For those stars much more massive than the sun Einstein's gravitational theory (general relativity) is applied.

Nicotinamide Adenine Dinucleotide: (NAD$^+$) Oxidized form of NAD. An enzyme which participates in the proton transport from inside to the intermembrance space of mitochondria.

Nihility: Part of existence bearing no manifestation.

Nitrogen: (N) *Chemistry*. a gaseous element having the symbol N, the atomic number 7, an atomic weight of 14.0067, a melting point of -209.9°C, and a boiling point of -195.5°C; a colorless, odorless, tasteless gas that makes up about four-fifths of the atmosphere; used in ammonia synthesis and as an inert gas, refrigerant, and fertilizer component. (From a French word for *niter,* or potassium nitrate.)

Nuclear Radius: Almost 1×10^{-13} cm where A is the atomic number or the protons number combined with the neutrons number in the nucleus.

Nuclear: A process in which the nucleus of an atom or at least one of its properties is involved.

Nucleon: A part of the atomic nucleus. In essence a proton or a neutron.

Nutritional Calorie: A unit of energy equivalent of one thermodynamical kilo calorie is equivalent with 4186 Joules of energy.

Orbits: The allowed paths of an object, e.g., electron in the field of another one, e.g., the proton in the hydrogen atom. The orbits in of the microscopic particles are also quantized, i.e., discrete.

Organ (body):   *Anatomy.* a structure containing two or more different cell types that are organized to carry out a particular function of the body, such as the heart or kidneys. *Botany.* a grouping of tissues into a distinct structure that performs a specialized task, such as a leaf or stamen.

Organelle: *Cell Biology.* a discrete body found in the cytoplasm of a cell, defined by a surrounding membrane, and performing a specific function.

Organic: *Chemistry.* of or relating to any covalently bonded compound containing carbon atoms. *Biology.* relating to or involving an organism or organisms. *Medicine.* relating to or affecting an organ of the body. *Agronomy.* of or relating to organic farming or organic foods.

Organic Molecule: Molecules containing carbon and hydrogen.

Organism: *Biology.* **1.** a living being; any form in which mutually interdependent parts maintain the various vital processes necessary for life to exist. **2.** a biological form considered as an entity, such as an animal, plant, or fungus.

Outer Space: The space beyond the Earth's upper atmosphere.

Oxidation: Any chemical reaction in which electrons are lost.

Oxygen: Chemistry. a gaseous element having the symbol O, the atomic number 8, atomic weight 15.9994, a melting point of -218.4°C, and a boiling point of -182.962°C; a colorless, odorless, tasteless gas that is the most abundant element on earth, making up about 20% by volume of the atmosphere at sea level, about 50% of the material of the earth's surface, and about 90% of water. Oxygen is necessary for the life processes of nearly all living organisms and for most forms of combustion. It readily forms compounds with nearly all other elements except the inert gases, and it is used in blast furnaces, steel manufacture, chemical synthesis, and in resuscitation, and for many other industrial purposes. (A word coined by the French chemist Antoine Lavoisier, literally meaning "acid producer;" from the belief of the time that oxygen is a component of all acids.)

Paralysis: Neurology. a temporary or permanent loss of motor function, especially loss of sensation or voluntary motion, generally caused by disease, dysfunction, or injury of the central nervous system or of the peripheral neuromuscular system.

Partial Pressure: *Physics.* the pressure of an individual gas that additively contributes to the total pressure in a gas mixture.

Particle Accelerator: Confines moving (usually electrically charged) particles by magnetic fields, $\vec{B}$ and accelerating them by electric fields, $\vec{E}$

Particle-Antiparticle: The pair that emerges out of a γ-ray photon entering the electron's (or the proton's) electrostatic field.

Particle's Wavelength: The wavelengths of the half waves or the full waves constructing the particle.

Pascal: **(P)** A unit of pressure, p (= force/area) equivalent with Newton/m^2 or kg/m.s^2.

Pathological: *Medicine.* **1.** relating to or caused by a disease or morbid process. **2.** of or relating to the field of pathology.of or relating to the field of pathology. *Psychology.* of behavior, caused by or showing evidence of a mental disorder. *Mathematics.* exhibiting behavior that is not typical of its class; however, one generation's pathological examples often become the next generation's standard mathematics.

Pelvis: Anatomy. the ring of bones forming a bowl in which the digestive organs are housed and to which the thigh bones are attached. Also, pelvic cavity.

Penetration Radius: The smallest radius to which the penetrating light (to the field of an electron or a proton) advances.

Perfusion: the act of perfusing; specific uses include: Physiology. the introduction of a fluid into an artery or vein. Surgery. 1. the passage of a liquid over or through an organ or tissue. 2. a liquid poured over or through an organ or tissue.

Period: (T) The time it takes for the oscillator to go through one complete oscillation.

Periodic Function: A function which repeats itself after

Peripheral Lymphoid Tissue: The lympoid tissue away from the center.

Peripheral Nervous System: *Anatomy.* the nervous system outside of the brain and spinal cord.

Permeability: Fluid Mechanics. the capability of a porous substance or membrane to allow a fluid to filter through it. Agronomy. the ease with which water, air, or plant roots penetrate or pass through a soil horizon. Engineering. the relative ability of a rock or soil to conduct magnetic lines of force. Electromagnetism. a factor that is characteristic of the magnetic properties of a substance; given by the ratio of the magnetic flux induction B to the magnetizing force H, and symbolized by μ ; in most cases, B is parallel to H and μ is a scalar quantity, otherwise m is a tensor.

Permeability of Space$\vec{E}$: The degree of the response of a space to permeate magnetic field.

Permittivity of Space: μ The degree of the response of a space to permeate electric field, $\vec{E}$.

Peter Mitchell: A British Biochemist first proposing the Chemiosmotic theory.

pH: *Chemistry.* a symbol for the logarithm of the reciprocal of the hydrogen-ion concentration of an aqueous solution, used to express its acidity or alkalinity. At 25°C (77°F), a neutral solution, such as pure water, has a pH of 7; a pH under 7 indicates that the solution is acidic, and a pH over 7 indicates that the solution is alkaline. (An abbreviation for potential of Hydrogen.)

Phagocytic Cell: A cell that is able to engulf and break down foreign particle cell debris, and desease producing microrganisms.

Phagocytosis: *Cell Biology.* the process by which certain phagocytes can ingest extracellular particles by engulfing them, functioning either in mammals as a defense mechanism against infection by microorganisms or in many protozoans as a means of taking up food particles.

Phase Velocity: The measure of the speed of the change of a, e.g., node to an antinode and again to a node, v_p.

Phosphates: Any salt of phosphoric acid H_3PO_4.

Phosphorilation: combining with phosphoros.

Photon: unit particle (of light) made of purely electromagnetic, E&M · radiation (oscillation).

Planet: One of the nine stars orbiting the sun. Any star orbiting a central star.

Plasma Protein: *Hematology.* any one of the hundreds of different proteins present in blood plasma, including carrier proteins, fibrinogen and other coagulation factors, immunoglobulins, enzyme inhibitors, and many other types of proteins.

Plastic Deformation: The long term or permanent displacement of the atoms (or molecules) from their normal sites in a solid (as a result of a force).

Platelets: the plural of Platelet, a cytoplasmic fragment that occurs in the blood of vertebrates and is associated with blood clotting. Also, THROMBOCYTE. *Hydrology.* one of the small ice crystals that join together to form a layer of floating ice and serve as seed crystals for the further thickening of the ice cover.

Polypeptide: *Biochemistry.* any of the class of compounds made up of a single chain of amino acid residues linked by peptide bonds, having a larger molecular weight than a peptide but less than a protein

Positron: The anti-particle of the electron.

Presynaptic and Postsynaptic Membranes: The axon membrance of one neuron and the dendrite membrane of the other.

Primary Cosmic Radiation: The particles arriving at the Earth's atmosphere from the outer space primarily all galaxies in the universe.   These particles are mainly comprised of Protons and the nuclei of the elements lighter than iron.

Principles of Special Relativity: The principles of special relativity are: All laws of physics are the same every inertial reference frame; The speed of light in vacuum (c = 3×10^8 m/s) measured in any inertial frame has always the same value of c regardless of the relative speeds of the inertial frames with respect to each other and that with respect to the light source.

Production of Light: The   matching   of   two   charged particles half waves (electromagnetic, E&M).

Protein: An elaborate nitrogenous macromolecule providing amino acids for the growth and repair of animal cells.

Proton Pool: A bundle of a lot of free protons.

Proton :   An elementary particle of mass 1.6726×10^{-27} kg ,electric charge 1.6×10^{-19} Coulomb, spin 1/2, and one of the contituents of the nucleus of atoms. Proton's natural lifetime is infinite unless it collides with other particles or atoms and splits to other elementary particles.

Protonation of F_0-F_1 Enzyme: The passage of the protons through knoblike F_0-F_1 Enzymes in order to synthesize ATP in mitochondrion respiration .

PSA (or PSA's) Theory: Professor Sadegh Angha ('s) theory of particle structure.

PSA Wave Equation: Professor Sadegh Angha's *unified* wave equation (for $\xi = \vec{E}.\vec{r}$ and/or $\vec{B}.\vec{r}$) which on the one hand reduces to the stationary state Schrodinger's (nonrelativistic) and Kline-Gordon (relativistic) equations and on the other hand is derived from the Maxwell's equations for the electric, $\vec{E}(\vec{r}, t)$ and magnetic, $\vec{B}(\vec{r}, t)$ fields in a variable permittivity, ($E=1/r^2$) environment. Thus unifying the quantum mechanical and electromagnetize fields.

Pulmonary: *Anatomy.* relating to or affecting the lungs.

Q Cycle: *Biochemistry.* a theoretical pathway first suggested in the respiratory loop model to explain certain phenomena, such as the extrusion of protons at complex III in the mitochondrial electron transport chain.

Quantized: Discontinuous, separate, partitioned elements of a particularly physical variable such as momentum, energy, electric charge, mass, magnetic moment, angular momentum, and etc.

Quantum Mechanical Variables: The discrete mechanical variables of the microscopic and submicroscopic particles

Quantum Number: Discontinuous (whole) number.

Radiation Energy: (RE) The energy in the full oscillation form resulting, e.g., from the matching of half oscillations of oppositely charged particles. The radiation energy of a particle, RE is $RE = Mv^2$ where M is the moving mass of the particle, i.e. $M = \dfrac{m_0}{\sqrt{1-\dfrac{v^2}{c^2}}}$.

Radiation Intensity: The number of the unit particles present in a radiation.

Radiation: Waves emerging from a source, e.g., thermal or an oscillating charge.

Random Motion: The motion of the microscopic particles as a result of their thermal kinetic energy. This motion does not have a specific direction thus generally takes place in every direction.

Reference Frame: The system of coordinates with respect to which all the observer's measurements are made.

Refractory Period: *Physiology.* a brief period of time following the stimulation of a nerve, during which the nerve cannot be restimulated. *Behavior.* a brief period of time following the initial movement of a set of similar movements in which a second movement cannot be initiated even if it is not antagonistic to the first. Also, **refractory phase.**

Regeneration: *Biology.* the growth of new tissues or organs to replace those lost or damaged by injury; this process is very variable in animals, being greatest in the lower animals, where a complete organism can sometimes be regenerated from a few cells, and least in the mammals, where it is limited to wound-healing and the regrowth of peripheral nerve fibers; it is a common occurrence in plants. *Computer Technology.* the process of restoring a computer storage element when its ability to store information deteriorates. *Control   Systems*.   see   POSITIVE FEEDBACK. *Electronics*.   see   REGENERATIVE FEEDBACK. *Nucleonics*. the treatment of used nuclear fuel elements so that they may be used again in the reactor.

Relativistic: In the realm of speeds comparable with that of light, c (c = $3X10^8$ m/s) or in the realm of strong field, i.e., object-field binding energies, w_B comparable with the mc^2 of the object itself.

Repolarization: The redistribution of the ions and electrons to two opposite sides of the substance.

Resistivity: (ρ) The electrical resistance, R of a unit length and unit area of a material.

Respiration: *Physiology*. the exchange of gases between the body and the atmosphere; the external and internal processes of breathing. The external, mechanical process involves the muscular activity of the lungs, bringing in oxygen that is absorbed by the blood (inhalation) and taking away waste gases from the blood (exhalation). The internal process allows the interchange of oxygen and carbon dioxide within the body cells, in which oxidation of food nutrients provides energy for cell activity and produces the waste materials of carbon dioxide and water.

Respiratory Cycle: One inhalation - exhaltion

Rest Mass: The total energy of an object, when stationary and out of any binding with any field, divided by the speed of light squared, In essence $m_0 = \dfrac{E_0}{C^2}$.

Rib: A member of the twelve pairs of bones that extend from the thoracic vertebrae to the sternum and form the walls of the thorax

Ribosome: The cellular submicroscopic location of receiving genetic information thereby synthesizing protein.

Ribs: the plural of Rib

Salt: Any compound resulting from acid-base reaction.

Sarcolema: The cell membrane of the muscle cell.

Sarcomere: The basic contractile unit of muscle (skeletal and cardiac) that structurally is the portion of a myofibril between two adjacent Z lines, the unit repeated along the entire length of the myofibril.

Sarcoplasm: The cytoplasmic matrix of muscle fibers

Saturate: to cause to become saturated or undergo saturation.

Saturation: the process of becoming or causing to become saturated, or the state of being saturated; specific uses include: *Physical Chemistry.* the condition of a solution in which it already has taken in the maximum possible amount of a solute under the given conditions. *Ecology.* a condition in which a given habitat is filled to capacity by individuals of a particular population in terms of the amount of resources needed to support the population. *Physics.* a condition of maximum effect in which any increase in a particular external influence will not result in an increase in the response. *Electromagnetism..* specifically, the condition in which a body of magnetic material subject to an increasing magnetic field does not undergo an increase in magnetization. *Electronics.* 1. a condition in which an input signal no longer generates a change in the output signal of a circuit. 2. the condition in which a transistor is driven so hard that its collector reverses itself and becomes positive with respect to the base instead of negative. *Nucleonics.* the condition of a nuclear reactor in which the production rate and the decay rate of a particular radionuclide are equal. *Optics.* a subjective perception of the percentage of white in a given color; low saturation indicates a large percentage of white, while high saturation indicates little or no white. Also, COLOR SATURATION.

Scalars: Physical quantities that can be identified only by one (mathematically real) number.

Schwartzchild Radius: A radius, r bellow which not even light (and therefore nothing else) can escape a black hole. In essence this $r = \dfrac{2GM}{c^2} = 3$ km.

Secondary Cosmic Radiation: Particles (elementary particles and photons) born out of the collision of the primary cosmic radiation and the upper atmospheric particles. This radiation mainly consists of π mesons, muons μ, neutrinos v, and electrons e. It is this secondary radiation which is received at the sea level.

Secretion: 1. the normal process by which various glands of the body release their substances. 2. such a substance produced by a gland; for example, sweat, digestive juices, bile, mucus, or saliva. Geology. a secondary structure formed from dissolved substances that are redeposited within an empty rock cavity, usually on or parallel to the cavity walls.

Self Energy: The (total) rest energy of the particle, mc^2 or the field self energy of the particle $e^2/2r$ at any point $\vec{r}$.

Sine Wave: A wave spatial and temporal propagation is sinusoidal. In essence the wave is shown as: $\sin(\vec{k}.\vec{r} + \omega t)$.

Slow Twitch Unit:

Soft Component of Cosmic Ray: The low energy part of the cosmic radiation which is absorbed before penetrating a lead plate of thickness 10 cm.

Solar Flares: Violent eruptions of heat ($T = 5 \times 10^6$ K), high-speed nuclei, electrons, and electromagnetic* radiation (from γ rays to radar waves) occurring in the solar atmosphere lasting for minutes to a few hours.

Solar System: The sun and those (nine) plants which due to their gravitational attraction to the sun orbit it.

Solid State Physics: That part of physics investigating the thermal, acoustical, electrical, and optical properties of solids. Nowadays this branch of physics is called Condensed Matter Physics mainly since those properties of liquids are also included. .

Solubility: The ability or tendency of one substance to dissolve into another at a given temperature and pressure; generally expressed in terms of the amount of solute that will dissolve in a given amount of solvent to produce a saturated solution.

Soma: The whole vegetative body of an organism, excluding the reproductive cells. *Physiology.* the body as distinguished from the mind. *Cell Biology.* a cell body.

Space-Time: A four dimensional system of coordinates three of which are indicative of spatial and the last one indicates the temporal measurements.

Special Relativity: A set of rules (and equations) connecting the measurements of observers moving at constant speeds with respect to one another and to the occurring event.

Spectroscopy: The study of the spectrum of the emitted or absorbed light through a source.

Spherical Coordinates: The length of, the angle with the z axis, and the angle with the x axis of the x-y (plane) component of the three dimensional position vector, $\vec{r}$ These three components characterizing the position vector $\vec{r}$ are shown by r, θ, and φ.

Spinal Cord: The column of nerve tissue that extends from the medulla oblongata through the canal created by the vertebral foramina of the vertebral column.

Spleen: The largest lymphatic organ in the body; it contains reticuloendothelial tissue and lies in the upper left part of the abdominal cavity, between the stomach and diaphragm; it serves as a reservoir of blood, disintegrates red blood cells, produces lymphocytes and plasma cells, and has other functions that are not fully understood. Also, splen.

Stationary Observer: An observer who has a relative zero speed, usually with respect to the being measured event.

Sternum: The long flat breastbone, consisting of three portions: the manubrium, body, and xiphoid process; articulates with the clavicles and with costal cartilages of the upper seven ribs. *Invertebrate Zoology.* **1.** the ventral plate or plates on each segment of an arthropod thorax. **2.** the ventral plates of the cuticle in members of the phylum Kinorhyncha.

Substrate: The structural surface beneath paint or other coverings. *Graphic Arts.* the paper or other surface upon which something is printed. *Electronics.* the support material on which an integrated circuit is constructed or to which it is attached. *Organic Chemistry.* a compound that reacts with a reagent. *Biochemistry.* the reactant in any enzyme-catalyzed reaction.

Substrate Molecules: The molecules which would go through the actual reaction.

Sulfur: (S) A nonmetallic element having the symbol S, the atomic number 16, and an atomic weight of 32.06; pure sulfur exists in two stable crystalline forms and in at least two liquid forms. *Mineralogy.* a yellow orthorhombic mineral that is the native form of this element; occurring as thick tabular or bipyramidal crystals and as granular to powdery masses, having a specific gravity of 2.07 and a hardness of 1.5 to 2.5 on the Mohs scale; found in volcanic or hot springs deposits, in sedimentary beds, and in salt domes; used in sulfuric acid production, in rubber vulcanization, and paper manufacture, and in gunpowder, fertilizers, and pharmaceuticals. (From the Latin name for this substance; its existence has been known since ancient times.) Also, SULPHUR

Surface Tension: The force of the surface molecules (of a liquid) on a each other or a foreign object.

Surfactant: Any surface-active agent or substance that modifies the nature of surfaces, often reducing the surface tension of water; surfactants are used as wetting agents, detergents, penetrants, and emulsifiers.

Synapse: A junctional site between two nerve cells, or between a nerve cell and a muscle or gland cell; the site where the electrical nerve impulse is converted to a chemical signal for transmission to the adjacent cell.

Synaptic Cleft: Has a length of 10-40 nm separates two neighboring neurons and acts as an insulator for the transmission of signals.

Synaptic Knob: The end part of the axon where it contacts the dendrite of other neuron.

Synthesis: The process of the fabrication of chemical compounds from more simple ones.

Tachypnea: A condition of excessively rapid respiration

Tensors: An array of n (rows) by m (columns) elements (either numbers or functions). For example the following is a 2 by 2 tensor $\begin{pmatrix} a & b \\ c & d \end{pmatrix}$.

The 20 Amino Acids: 55% of the atoms present in the amino acids are H atoms

The Evolutionary Model: A theory of the solar system formation on the basis of it being scattered dust particles integrating the planets and the sun due to their mutual gravitational attraction.

The Speed of Light: Is, c = 3X10^8 m/s in vacuum and changes to a usually smaller constants in other environments.

The trapped Radiation Energy: The kinetic energy of a particle or the Binding energy of any two objects.

The Untangling of Negative and Positive Oscillations:
The reception of the tradable (the binding) energy thus leaving each others bond.

Theoretical Science: That part of science that have been confirmed logically, mathematically (where possible), and experimentally.

Therapeutic: 1. acting as a cure or a relief; curative.acting as a cure or a relief; curative. 2. of or relating to therapeutics.of or relating to therapeutics.

Thermal Energy: A form of energy manifesting as the atomic kinetic energy

Thermal Equilibrium: Being at the same temperature.

Thermal Velocity: The velocity of the atoms or the electrons in random directions. Often this random motion is due to the thermal energy of the system.

Thermodynamics: The physical laws governing the thermal behavior of systems.
These cells contain the code for the production of surfactant

Threshold Potential: The best upper (or greatest lower) potential effects.

Tides: The Earth surface deformation due to the Moon's gravitational effects.

Time Dilation: The apparent relativistic slow down in the time of a relatively moving clock. In essence

$$t = t_0 \Big/ \sqrt{1 - \frac{v^2}{c^2}} \quad .$$

Time Dilation: The slower passage of time in a relatively fast ($v \cdot c = 3 \times 10^8$ m/s) moving frame of reference or that in the frame of a tightly bound object (object-field binding energy, w_B comparable with the mc^2 of the object itself).

Tonsil: A small, rounded mass of lymphatic tissue located in the pharynx and fauces. Also, tonsilla.

Tonsils: The plural of Tonsils

Trachea: plural, tracheae. *Anatomy.* the air tube supported by cartilaginous rings that stretches from the pharynx into the thorax, where it divides into the bronchial tubes. *Invertebrate Zoology.* any of the air-conveying tubules composing the complex branched respiratory system in insects, myriapods, and some arachnids. Botany. a vascular conducting tube located in the xylem.

Tradable Energy: Part of the radiation energy, RE which can leave the system (of the matched particles or that of the matched particle and a field).

Transition Zone: 1. the region of the earth's upper mantle, equivalent to the C layer, in which density and seismic-wave velocities increase. 2. the region within the earth's outer core, equivalent to the F layer, that is transitional to the inner core. *Fluid Mechanics.* the limited region in which flow changes from laminar to turbulent.

Trapped Energy: That part of the radiation energy, RE which does not emerge the system.

Tritium: (T) An isotope of the hydrogen atom. A hydrogen atom with two extra neutrons at its nucleus. Therefore a Tritium nucleus contains one proton and two neutrons.

Troponin: A omplex of three polypeptide chains that mediates calcium's effect on muscle contraction.

Tumor: 1. an abnormal growth that arises from normal tissue, but that grows abnormally both in rate and structure and serves no physiological function. Also, NEOPLASM.an abnormal growth that arises from normal tissue, but that grows abnormally both in rate and structure and serves no physiological function. Also, NEOPLASM. 2. a swelling or enlargement; one of the cardinal signs of inflammation.

Ubiquinone Molecules (Coenzyme Q): A compound that is structurally related to vitamin K and that functions as an electron carrier in the electron transport system of cells. Also, UBIQUINONE.

Upper Atmosphere: Mainly constituted by the ionosphere in which the due to the intense sun's ultraviolet and X-radiation atoms are ionized. The most abundant ions in the Earth's atmosphere are N_2 (78%) and O_2 (21%).

Vectors: Physical quantities that can be identified at least by two (mathematically real) numbers.

Ventilation: The circulation and purification of air in an enclosed space. *Meteorology.* the process of exposing a weather-observation instrumentation to a flow of air.

Vertebrae: Any bone that make the main body in mammals.

Vesicle: 1. a small cavity or sac usually containing fluid, as a blister. 2. small globular or bladderlike air spaces in tissues.. 3. one of three primary cavities of the brain. *Geology.* a small cavity in lava formed by the entrapment of a gas bubble during solidification of lava. Also, VACUOLE.

Virus: A noncellular microbial entity that consists of a core of RNA or DNA enclosed in an outer coat of protein and, in some forms, a protective outer membrane, and that can live and reproduce only in susceptible host cells. Viruses infect bacteria, plants, and animals, and more than 200 types have been identified as capable of causing diseases in humans, such as influenza, the common cold, measles, smallpox, and herpes

Viscosity: The degree of the molecular adhesion of a substance. On the molecular level viscosity, η indicates the average ability of the molecules to bind (cling to) any other molecules in the system.

Volume: The amount of space an object occupies.

Watt: (W) The unit of power, P defined as the time rate change of energy, W. In essence $P = \dfrac{dW}{dt}$.

Wave Propagation: The advancement of a wave in space.

White Cell (leukocyte): A white or colorless cell of the blood, having a nucleus and either granular or nongranular cytoplasm; leukocytes function as bacterial or viral phagocytes, as detoxifiers of toxic proteins, and in the development of immunities. Also, WHITE BLOOD CELL.

White Dwarf: A small (m<mass of the sun) hot star that has ended its life sequence.

Work: The product of displacement and the component of the force along the displacement, Fcosθ. in essence, W = dFcos(**W**) where W is the work, d is the displacement, F is the force producing the displacement, and θ is the angle between the force and the displacement.

γ Rays: Electromagnetic, E&M radiation with frequencies bigger than $1X10^{18}$ Hz.

μ Meson: The same as muon.

μ Muon: A subatomic particle of mass approximately 210 times that of the electron (m=$9.1X10^{-31}$kg), an electric charge of zero or ẽ (=-$1.6X10^{-19}$C), and a lifetime of $2.2X10^{-6}$sec.

References and Footnotes

Chapter 1

1.   David G. Nicholls and Stuart J. Ferguson,

      Bioenergetics 2, (Academic Press, Ca 1992).

2.   Wayne M. Becker, The World of the Cell

      (Benjamin/Cummings, Menlo Park, Ca 1986).

3.   Robert Roskoski, Jr., Biochemistry (W.B. Saunders,

      Philadelphia, Pa 1996).

4.   For a good review see Y. Hatefi, The Mitochondrial

      Electron Transport Chain and Oxidative Phosphorilation

      System, Annual Review of Biochemistry, 54, 1015-1069

      1985).

5.   Ei-Ichiro Ochiai, General Principlesof Biochemistry of

      Elements (Plenum Press, New York   1987).

6.   Peter C. Hinkle and Richard E. McCarty, How

Cells Make ATP, Scientific American, March (1978).

7. Agamemnon Despopoulos and Stephan Silbernagl, Color Atlas of Physiology (Thieme, New York 1991).

8. Paul D. Boyer, Britton Cance, Lars Ernster, Peter Mitchell, Efraim Racker, and E.C.Slater, Annual Review of Biochemistry, 46, 955-1026 (1977).

9. Johann Rafelski and Steven E. Jones, Cold Nuclear Fusion, Scientific American, July (1987).

10. Paul G. Hewitt, Conceptual Physics (Harper Collins Publisher, 1989).

11. David R. Lide, Editor, CRC Handbook of Chemistry and Physics 71st Ed. (CRC Press, Ann Arbor 1990-1991).

12. J. E. Hooper and M. Scharf, The Cosmic Radiation (John Wiley & Sons, New York 1958).

13.   S. Hayakawa, <u>Cosmic Ray Physics</u> (John Wiley & Sons, New York 1969).

14.   H. R. Hulme, <u>Nuclear Fusion</u> (Springer-Verlag, New York 1969).

15.   Eldon J. Gardner and D. Peter Snustad, <u>Principles of Genetics</u> (John Wiley & Sons, 1984). The 1.724 g/cm is taken as the density of E.coli DNA in this reference.

16.   Frank Close, <u>Too Hot to Handle, The Race For Cold Fusion</u> (Princeton University Press, Princeton, NJ 1991).

17.   Ralph H. Petrucci, <u>General Chemistry, Principles and Modern Applications</u> (Macmillan, New York 1982, Fourth Edition).

18.   Professor Sadegh Angha, <u>The Hidden Angles of Life</u> (Multidisciplinary Publications, Pomona, Ca 1975).

Chapter 2

1. Robert Roskoski, Jr. Biochemistry (Sunders, Philadelphia 1996).

2. Wayne M. Becker, The World of the Cell, (Benjamin/Cummings, Menlo Park, Ca 1986).

3. Ralph H. Petrucci, General Chemistry, Principles and Modern Applications (Macmillan, New York 1982, Fourth Edition).

4. Agamemnon Despopoulos and Stephan Silbernagl, Color Atlas of Physiology, (Thieme, New York 1991).

5. John R. Reitz and Frederick J. Milford, Foundations of Electromagnetic Theory, (Addison-Wesley, Reading, Mass. 1962)

6. David E. Martin and John W. Youtsey, Respiratory Anatomy and Physiology, (Mosby, St. Louis 1988).

7. Johann Rafelski and Steven E. Jones, Cold Nuclear Fusion, Scientific American, July (1987).

8. J. E. Hooper and M. Scharf, <u>The Cosmic Radiation</u> (John Wiley & Sons, New York 1958).

9. Professor Sadegh Angha, <u>The Epic of Life</u>, (M.T.O. Shahmaghsoudi, Tehran 1979).

10. Professor Sadegh Angha, <u>The Hidden Angles of</u> Life, (Multidisciplinary Publications, Pomona, Ca. 1975).

11. Albert Szent-Gyorgyi <u>The Living State and Cancer</u> (Marcel Decker, Inc., New York 1978).

12. Albert Szent-Gyorgyi <u>Electronic Biology and</u> Cancer (Marcel Decker Inc., New York 1976).

13. Albert Szent-Gyorgyi, <u>The Living State With</u> Observation <u>on Cancer</u> (Academic Press, New York 1972).

14. Albert Szent-Gyorgyi, <u>Bioelectronics</u> (Academic Press, New York 1968).

Chapter 3

1. Professor Sadegh Angha and Dr. Sirus Aryainejad, Professor Sadegh Angha's Theory of Particle Structure and Its Application, (Vantage Press, New York 1994).

2. F. K. Richtmyer, E. H. Kennard, and J. N. Cooper, Introduction to Modern Physics, (Mc Graw Hill, New York 1969).

3. H. R. Hulme, Nuclear Fusion, (Springer-Verlag, 1969 London).

4. For a more elaborate and mathematical treatment of this in the case of the H atom, refer to chapter two of reference one.

5. Max Born, Atomic Physics, (Blackie & Son Limited, Glasgow 1969).

6.   Micheal W. Friedlander, <u>Astronomy; From Stone Age to Quasars</u> (Prentice-Hall, New Jersey 1985).

7.   George Gamow, <u>Matter, Earth, and Sky</u> (Prentice-Hall, New Jersey, 1958).

8.   Hans C. Ohanian, <u>Gravitation and Spacetime</u> (W.W. Norton & Company, New York 1976).

9.   A. P. French, <u>Special Relativity</u> (W. W. Norton & Company New York 1968).

10.   Professor Sadegh Angha, <u>The Epic of Life</u> (M.T.O. Shahmaghsoudi, Tehran 1979).

11.   Hazrat Molana Shahmaghsoud Sadegh Angha, <u>The Principles of Faghr and Sufism</u> (M.T.O. Shahmaghsoudi, Verdugo City CA 1987).

12.   Lord   Mir Ghotbeddin Mohammad Angha, <u>Az Janin</u>

       <u>Ta Janan (From the Womb to Heaven)</u> (M.T.O.

       Shahmaghsoudi, Tehran 1982).

13.   Hazrat Molana Shahmaghsoud Sadegh Angha,

       <u>Chanteh (The Gnostic's Cosmos),</u> (M.T.O.

       Shahmaghsoudi, Verdugo City CA 1988).

14.   Philip M. Morse, Herman Feshbach, <u>Methods of</u>

       <u>Mathematical Physics,</u> (Mc Graw Hill, New York

       1953).

Chapter 4

1.　　Agamemnon Despopoulos and Stefan Silbernagl,

　　　Color Atlas of Physiology (Thieme Medical

　　　Publishers, Inc., New York　　1991).

2.　　Richard M. Restak, The Mind (Bantam Books, New

　　　York 1988).

3.　　Raphael H. Rhodes, Hypnosis (MJF Books, New

　　　York 1978).

4.　　Daniel Johnston and Samuel Miao-Sin Wu,

　　　Foundations of Cellular Neurophysiology (The MIT

　　　Press, Cambridge, Massachusetts 1997).

5.　　J. J. B. Jack, D. Noble, and R. W. Tsien, Electric

　　　Current Flow in Excitable Cells (Clarendon Press,

　　　Oxford 1975).

6.　　David J. Aidely, The Physiology of Excitable Cells

Second Edition, (Cambridge University Press,

Cambridge. 1978).

7.   A. L. Hodjkin and A. F. Huxley, The Journal of

Physiology, 117, 500 -44 (1952).

8.   Wayne M. Becker, <u>The World of the Cell</u> (The

Benjamin/Commings, Menlo Park, Ca 1986).

9.   John R. Reitz and Fredrerick J. Milford, <u>Foundations

of Electromagnetic Theory</u> (Addison-Wesley,

Reading, Mass. 1962).

10.   Steven Pinker, <u>How the Mind Works</u> (W. W.   Norton

& Company, New York 1997).

11.   Professor Sadegh Angha, <u>The Hidden Angles of Life</u>

(Multidisciplinary Publications, Pomona, California

1975).

12.   Professor Sadegh Angha, <u>Manifestation of Thought</u>

(University Press of America, Inc., MD 1988).

13.   J. Bardeen, L. N. Cooper, and J. R. Shrieffer, Phys. Rev. **108**, 1175 (1957).

14.   Philip W. Anderson and Robert Schrieffer, Phys. Today, **44**, 54 (1991).

15.   E. A. Lynton, <u>Superconductivity,</u> (John Wiley& Sons, New York 1962).

16.   Gerald Burns, <u>High - Temperature Superconductivity, An Introduction,</u> (Academic   Press, Boston 1992).

17.   Charles Kittel, <u>Introduction to Solid StatePhysics,</u> (John Wiley & Sons, New York 1986).

18.   Neil W. Ashcroft and N. David Mermin, <u>Solid State Physics,</u> (Sanders, Philadelphia 1976).

19.   Vladimir Z. Kresin, Hans Morowitz, and Stuart A.

Wolf, <u>Mechanisms of Conventional and High-Tc Superconductivity,</u> (Oxford University Press, New York 1993).

20. Nikolai M. Plakida, <u>High-Temperature Superconductivity, Experiment and Theory,</u> (Springer-Verlag, New York 1995).

21. S. Pan *et al.* , Phys. Rev. **B 35**, 7220   (1987).

22. M. E. Hawley *et al.* , Phys. Rev. **B 35**, 7224 (1987).

23. A. Junod, in <u>Physical Properties of High Temperature Superconductors,</u> ed. by D.M. Ginsberg (World Scientific, Singapore 1990) v2, p. 13.

24. Bertram Batlogg, Phys. Today, **44**, 44 (1991).

25. F. W. de Wette *et al.* , Phys. Rev. **B 42**, 6707 (1990).

26. T. Laegreid, K. Fossheim, and F. Vassenden, Physica

484

EXPANSION AND CONTRACTION WITHIN BEING

C153-155, 1096 (1988).

27. P.B. Allen, in Physical Properties of High Temperature Superconductors, ed. by D.M. Ginsberg (World Scientific, Singapore 1990) v 1, p. 213.

28. R. Micnas, J. Ranninger, S. Robaszkiewicz, Rev. Mod. Phys. **62**, 113 (1990).

29. A. Fisher, J. E. Gordon, N. E. Phyllips, J. Superconduct. **1**, 231 (1988).

30. W. K. Kwok *et al.* , Phys. Rev. **B 35**, 5343 (1987).

31. R.J. Cava *et al.* , Phys. Rev. Lett. **58**, 1676 (1987).

32. A. J. Panson *et al.* , Phys. Rev. **B 35**, 8774 (1987).

33. B. D. Dunlap *et al.*, Phys. Rev. **B 35**, 7210 (1987).

34. we have $\dfrac{v_F}{v_s} \dfrac{U_{ph}}{\eta\, k_B\, T} \approx \dfrac{v_F}{v_s} \dfrac{3\,\pi^4}{\eta} \left(\dfrac{T}{\theta_D}\right)^3$

Taking $v_F = 1 \times 10^7$ cms^{-1}, $v_s = 5 \times 10^5$ cms^{-1}, $\eta = 7$, $\theta_D = 400$ K, and 40 K $< T_c <$ 80 K, we obtain $0.8 < \dfrac{v_F}{v_s} \dfrac{3\,\pi^4}{\eta} \left(\dfrac{T}{\theta_D}\right)^3 < 6.7$

almost of the order of unity.

35. A.P. Malozemoff, in <u>Physical Properties of High Temperature Superconductors,</u> ed. By D.M. Ginsberg (World Scientific, Singapore 1990) v.1,   p. 71.

36. P.S. Angha and S. Aryainejad, <u>Professor Sadegh Angha's Theory of Particle Structure and Its Applications,</u> (Vantage Press, New York 1990).

NOTES:

Corrections:

Page	Line	Incorrect	Correct
121	2	Nm^2/Kg^2	Nm^2/c^2
171	1	W_B	W_B
180	12	$W_0/2 = 13.6/2 = 6.8$	$2W_0/2 = 13.6$
181	8	Therefore	Since
247	5	$v_p = M v^2/p$	$v_p = M v^2/p = \hbar\omega/\hbar k$
301	(26)	X	x
307	(40)	$\varepsilon_L . L_L$	$\varepsilon_L - L_L$
310	(47)	$I_\lambda = - I_C$	$I_\lambda = - I_c$
334	5	$\Delta t' = \Delta t / \left(1 - \dfrac{v^2}{c^2}\right)^{-1/2}$	$\Delta t' = \Delta t / \left(1 - \dfrac{v^2}{c^2}\right)^{1/2}$
353	2	$\phi + \pi$	$\phi + 2\pi$
369	2	electron $_\lambda$Th. e	electron λTh. e
369	3	$_\lambda$Th. e	λTh. e
375	9	$T_c \propto M^{-4/7}$	$T_c \propto M^{-4/7}$
416	2	about 1mm	about 1 μm
420	16	78.5° C	− 78.5° C
421	19	**Cell Membrane Electric Potential Difference: (EPD)** The potential difference	**Cell Membrane Electric Potential Difference: (EPD)** The potential difference between the cell inner and outer membranes (about 60mv with the inner layer being negative).

Page	Line	Incorrect	Correct
421	21	**Cell Proliferation:** Cell division between the cell inner.....layer being nega.	**Cell Proliferation:** Cell division
423	8	T $\mid$ 1000 K	T $\approx$ 1000 K
425	23	embedded the	embedded in the
430	8	charge of 1.6×10^{-19}	charge of -1.6×10^{-19}
441	4	in essence:	*(joins previous line)*
444	13	$M = m_0 / \sqrt{1 - \dfrac{v^2}{c^2}}$	$M = m_0 \Big/ \sqrt{1 - \dfrac{v^2}{c^2}}$
446	23	10-100 mm	10-100 μm
449	22	1×10^{-13} cm	$1 \times 10^{-13} A^{1/3}$ cm
453	12	otherwise m is	otherwise μ is
453	13	space $\vec{E}$	space μ
453	15	permittivity of space μ	permittivity of space ε
456	12	$(E = 1/r^2)$	$(\varepsilon \alpha\ 1/r)$
466	5	$(v: c = 3 \times 10^8$ m/s$)$	$(v \approx c = 3 \times 10^8$ m/s$)$
469	5	dFcos (W)	dFcos (θ)

NOTES: